INSTRUCTOR'S RESOURCE MANUAL
PREPARED BY R. L. KERNELL

JOHN D. CUTNELL   KENNETH W. JOHNSON

PHYSICS

WILEY

JOHN WILEY & SONS

NEW YORK CHICHESTER BRISBANE TORONTO SINGAPORE

CONTENTS

P H Y S I C S

INTRODUCTION

This instructor's resource manual is designed to accompany *Physics* by John D. Cutnell and Kenneth W. Johnson (John Wiley & Sons, 1989), a book that contains 39 chapters and is intended for the course usually referred to as *College Physics*. This non-calculus level course assumes that students have a knowledge of algebra and are familiar with simple relations from trigonometry. For each chapter of the text, this resource manual contains the following:

A list of **Transparencies (acetates)** for that chapter. These are full size, two-color transparencies made from selected diagrams (figures) in the text; there are a total of 100.

Solved Problems. This is a list of problems in that chapter that are solved in detail in the *Study Guide* by Charles R. McKenzie and Andrew J. Pica in collaboration with the authors of the primary text. The *Study Guide* is keyed to the text and is intended to be of assistance in encouraging and motivating students and in helping them in the course.

Spreadsheets suitable for use by students in studying the material in the particular chapter. These refer to the supplement *Wondering About Physics...Using Spreadsheets to Find Out* by Dewey I. Dykstra, Jr. and Robert G. Fuller (John Wiley & Sons, 1988).

Demonstrations appropriate for material in the chapter. Each chapter has references to demonstrations selected from three widely used demonstration resource books (see subsequent section for details). In addition, for most chapters I have given instructions for performing a few relatively simple demonstrations that I have found to be effective.

Films are listed for most chapters. The format, length, and source of each film is shown; addresses of sources are given in a separate compilation. Also listed under films are titles from *What If...?* by Fuller and Dykstra (John Wiley & Sons, 1988). This consists of 16 two-minute videotape vignettes depicting physical phenomena that can't be demonstrated in the classroom or seen with the naked eye.

Laboratory experiments are listed for two laboratory manuals published by John Wiley. These are: *Laboratory Experiments in College Physics*, Sixth Edition, by Cicero H. Bernard and Chirold D. Epp and *Experiments in Physics* by Daryl W. Preston, Joseph W. Kane, and Morton W. Sternheim. The first manual is a comprehensive one containing 50 experiments; the second manual features 27 experiments of which more than a third have a biological science emphasis.

Computer Resources suitable for the chapter. The nature of the listings under this category is described in detail in a subsequent section.

Lecture Notes are given for each chapter. These are presented in outline form and consist largely of the main and secondary headings of the various sections in each chapter. Generous space is allowed on the outline for each instructor to make his/her own detailed outline according to individual preferences. For most chapters the Lecture Notes are three pages long. An additional page, entitled **Next Time Notes** is included following the Lecture Notes. This may be helpful for making notes on (1) what went well with various items (demonstrations, examples, films, etc) and (2) anything else that you may want to remember for next time.

In addition to the resources listed with the individual chapters, this manual contains several items of a more general nature. These are:

Textbook Conversion Notes. These notes compare the book by Cutnell and Johnson with four other books that are rather widely used as texts in College Physics courses. This section is intended to assist physics instructors in considering texts for adoption for their classes.

Suggested Courses. Syllabi used in College Physics classes on a variety of campuses throughout the nation have been examined with a view to preparing a suggested schedule appropriate for a one-year course given under either the semester or the quarter system. Discussion is given regarding allocation of lecture time to the 39 chapters in the text.

Ideas for the First Time Lecturer. The Physics Editor of John Wiley insisted that I write several pages that purport to be "what an experienced/successful College Physics instructor would relate to a colleague teaching the course for the first time." Her insistence and my persistence have resulted in the jottings that constitute this section of the resource manual.

4

Three additional supplements that are coordinated with the text are available. These are:

Solutions Manual by Charles R. McKenzie and Andrew J. Pica. This manual is available only to instructors; it contains detailed solutions to all problems in the text in a form suitable for posting or for preparing transparencies to use in class or review sessions.

Test Bank by Jack H. Noon. This contains over 1200 essay questions, short answer questions, and problems.

Computerized Test Bank consists of IBM, Apple II, and Macintosh versions of the entire Test Bank with full editing features to help you customize your tests.

As you can see, an impressive set of supplements is available to support the primary text. I hope that this instructor's resource manual will be useful to those who struggle to enlighten today's generation of students about physics. I express appreciation to Dr. Jacob Becher, Old Dominion University, for preparing the Textbook Conversion Notes and for helpful discussions and to Dr. J. Richard Christman, United States Coast Guard Academy, for substantial assistance in preparing the Computer Resources section.

R L Kernell

Robert Lee Kernell
Old Dominion University
December 1988

TEXTBOOK CONVERSION NOTES: DISCUSSION

This section compares the topic coverage in the new algebra/trigonometry text by John Cutnell and Kenneth Johnson with that in four textbooks that are rather widely used in College Physics. This comparison will be useful to those choosing a text for such a course. The books compared are:

> *Physics* by Cutnell and Johnson
> *Principles of Physics (2nd ed.)* by Blatt
> *Physics (2nd ed.)* by Giancoli
> *College Physics* by Serway and Faughn
> *College Physics* by Tipler

We will refer to these as C/J, B, G, S/F, and T. After giving a general overview of these texts, we will present a detailed list of topics together with specific pages on which each topic is covered in these five books.

> The subject matter in all of these books is divided into six sections:
>> mechanics
>> thermal physics
>> wave motion and sound
>> electricity and magnetism
>> optics
>> modern physics

The first three sections are usually covered in the first semester and the latter three sections in the second semester. There is complete uniformity among these five books in the allocation of topics to a given semester. Thus it convenient to make comparisons among the books on a semester by semester basis. With regard to the first semester, the allocation of topics among the three sections (mechanics, thermal physics, and wave motion and sound) is generally the same in all five texts except that C/J covers simple harmonic motion in the mechanics section (in connection with elastic properties of matter) while the other four texts treat simple harmonic motion in the section on wave motion and sound. Let us now consider each of these three sections individually.

The chief difference in the ordering of topics in the mechanics section involves gravitation, uniform circular motion, and rotational equilibrium. The different ordering of these three topics is due partly to the view of some authors that it is often more effective to give a preliminary discussion of particular topics early in the text and then to revisit these topics in connection with subject matter in later chapters. For example, C/J introduces gravitation in a general discussion of types of forces given immediately after covering Newton's Laws of motion and then revisits gravitation when uniform circular motion is considered. B, G, and S/F present all of their coverage of gravitation in connection with uniform circular motion while T introduces gravitation after having treated rotational dynamics and energy. C/J, G, and T introduce uniform circular motion (to include dynamics) in the discussion of translational motion and then revisit uniform circular motion in their coverage of rotation. B and S/F postpone discussion of uniform circular motion until after rotational motion has been introduced. S/F and T introduce torque and rotational equilibrium immediately after treating translational equilibrium and revisit torque when rotational motion is considered. C/J, B, and G postpone rotational equilibrium problems and the concept of torque to the chapter on rotational dynamics.

All five books begin the thermal physics section by defining temperature and discussing temperature scales. Four texts (C/J, B, G, and S/F) then introduce thermal expansion. A divergence occurs here in that C/J and B cover calorimetry, heat transfer, the ideal gas law, kinetic theory, and laws of thermodynamics while G and S/F discuss the ideal gas law and kinetic theory before covering the other topics. A considerably different sequence is used by T: temperature is followed by the ideal gas law, kinetic theory, calorimetry, first law of thermodynamics, thermal expansion, heat transfer, and the second law of thermodynamics. The five books follow essentially the same sequence in the section on wave motion and sound except that C/J has already discussed simple harmonic motion in the mechanics section.

Turning now to the second semester, the allocation of topics among the three sections (electricity and magnetism, optics, and modern physics) is nearly the same in all five books except that C/J and S/F discuss semiconductor devices in the section on electricity and magnetism (in the alternating currents chapter) while B, G, and T postpone a consideration of semiconductors to the modern physics section. Let us now consider each of these three sections one by one.

There are two primary variations in the ordering of topics in the section on electricity and magnetism. These are: (1) capacitors in series and parallel and (2) construction of ammeters and voltmeters from galvanometers. With regard to capacitance, all five books introduce the concept of capacitance immediately after discussing the electrostatic potential. B, S/F, and T proceed immediately to cover series and parallel capacitors whereas C/J and G postpone discussing combinations of capacitors to the chapter on electric circuits. Four of the books (C/J, B, G, and T) treat the construction of voltmeters and ammeters from galvanometers in the electric circuits chapter while S/F postpones this topic to the chapter on the interaction of currents with magnetic fields.

The five books are similar in their treatment of optics, the primary difference being that C/J, B, and T discuss optical instruments before wave optics while G and S/F cover optical instruments after wave optics and thus are able to treat wave-dependent characteristics of some optical instruments.

Special relativity is the first topic covered in the modern physics section of each of the five books. This is followed by a discussion of phenomena and theories that culminated in quantum mechanics. Other topics covered are atomic and molecular theory, solids, nuclear structure, radioactivity, and elementary particles. The primary difference in this section is that C/J and S/F do not include a discussion of molecular bonding and the band theory of solids whereas the other three books treat these topics at varied lengths to include coverage of semiconductor devices. As previously noted, C/J and S/F discuss semiconductor devices in the electricity section.

TABLE FOR TEXTBOOK CONVERSION NOTES

This table presents a listing of topics and the pages on which these topics are covered in the following five textbooks:

Physics	Cutnell and Johnson	**C/J**
Principles of Physics (2nd ed)	Blatt	**B**
Physics (2nd ed.)	Giancoli	**G**
College Physics	Serway and Faughn	**S/F**
College Physics	Tipler	**T**

TOPIC	C/J	B	G	S/F	T
Mechanics:					
Introduction, Units	1-6	1-5	1-10	1-13	1-12
Mathematics, Scalars, Vectors	6-17	6-14	12-13 30-35	13-20	36-41
Kinematics in One Dimension	22-45	17-29	10-26	25-37	15-30
Kinematics in Two Dimensions	50-64	29-41	35-43	37-44	41-49
Newton's Laws	70-78	46-51	47-56	50-60	58-68
Gravitational Force	78-83	138-147	78-89	153-160	198-219
Application of Newton's Laws	83-107	51-66	56-66	60-71	69-79 87-92
Uniform Circular Motion	113-126	127-133	69-78	147-152	49-52 100-107
Work, Energy, and Power	131-149	74-93	94-112	97-115	113-141
Impulse and Momentum	156-168	98-118	117-132	121-135	147-168
Rotational Kinematics	173-186	122-127	137-141	140-147	174-177
Torque, Rotational Equilibrium	192-202	149-156	142-144 160-166	76-91	92-100
Rotational Dynamics	202-214	156-170	144-155	164-176	177-192
Properties of Matter	224-229	178-195	169-174	181-187	223-226
Simple Harmonic Motion	230-245	310-328	294-304	310-324	352-369

TOPIC	C/J	B	G	S/F	T
Mechanics: (continued)					
Fluid Statics	252-266	199-213	184-201	187-200	227-238
Fluid Dynamics	273-289	213-230	201-213	205-223	239-247
Thermal Physics:					
Temperature, Thermal Expansion	293-305	237-246	217-224	229-237	253-259 292-296
Heat Energy and Phase Changes	309-325	246-251	250-259	254-264	270-275 296-303
Transfer of Heat	329-344	251-261	259-267	264-278	304-317
Ideal Gas Law, Kinetic Theory	348-363	266-284	224-245	237-249	259-267
Thermodynamics Law I	368-381	288-294	271-275	283-290	275-289
Thermodynamics Law II	386-403	294-307	275-290	290-303	324-347
Wave Motion:					
Introduction to Waves	410-418	333-338	305-315	324-330	373-383
Sound, Doppler Effect	421-438	356-372	325-343	339-351	384-396
Interference, Diffraction	445-463	339-352	315-320	330-333	400-420 351-360
Electricity and Magnetism:					
Electric Forces and Fields	468-490	380-407	353-371	373-390	423-442
Electric Potential	495-511	407-439	374-389	395-404	453-473
Electric Current; Resistance	518-530	447-454	392-405	420-433	488-504
Electric Circuits	534-550	455-480	412-433	437-457	504-522
Series and Parallel Capacitors	546-548	439-443	420-422	404-415	474-479

DEMONSTRATIONS

There are several excellent books on demonstrations suitable for the introductory physics course. The TEACHING AIDS page for each chapter lists some demonstrations from the following three books:

A Demonstration Handbook for Physics, G.D. Freier and F.J. Anderson, 320 pages, 1981. Contains instructions (with line drawings) for 807 demonstrations, many of which can be set up using simple equipment. Available from American Association of Physics Teachers, 5110 Roanoke Place, College Park, MD 20740.

Physics Demonstration Experiments at William Jewell College, Wallace A. Hilton, 112 pages, 1982. More than 300 demonstrations are described. Available from AAPT at the address given above.

Physics Demonstration Experiments, Harry F. Meiners, ed. Published in 1970. This two-volume work of more than 1300 pages is an excellent source of information on specific demonstrations as well as general articles that discuss the philosophy and techniques of lecture demonstrations. Available from Robert E. Krieger Publishing Company, Malabar, FL 32950.

Other publications and books that are useful are:

Resource Letter PhD-1: Physics Demonstrations, J.A. Davis and B.G. Eaton, 6 pages, 1979. Has 103 references to books and monographs that deal with physics demonstrations. Available from AAPT at the address given above.

Apparatus for Teaching Physics, reprinted from *The Physics Teacher*, American Association of Physics Teachers, 1972.

Apparatus Notes, reprinted from *American Journal of Physics*, 1965-72, American Association of Physics Teachers, 1972.

Demonstration Experiments in Physics, Richard M. Sutton, McGraw-Hill, New York, 1938.

Demonstrations in Physics, Julius Sumner Miller, Ure Smith, London, 1969.

Experiments and Demonstrations in Optics, C. Harvey Palmer, Johns Hopkins University Press, Baltimore, 1962.

Exploring Laser Light, T. Kallard. Available from AAPT at address given above, 1977.

Phenomenal Physics, Clifford E. Swartz, John Wiley, New York, 1981.

Physics Demonstrations and Experiments for High School, Gordon E. Jones, Physics Department, Mississippi State University, Mississippi State, MS 39762,

KEY TO FILM SOURCES

AAPT American Association of Physics Teachers
5110 Roanoke Place, College Park, MD 20740

ACAY Academy Films
Box 1023, Venice, CA 90291

AEF American Educational Films
132 Lasky Dr., P.O. Box 5001
Beverly Hills, CA 90212

AIMS Aims Distribution Media Services, Inc.
P.O. Box 1010, Hollywood, CA 90028

BAY Around the Bay
1140 Irving St., San Francisco, CA 94122

BFA BFA Educational Media
Div. Of Columbia Broadcasting System
2211 Michigan Ave., P.O. Box 1795
Santa Monica, CA 90406

BTL Bell Telephone Laboratories
Film Library, Murray Hill, N.J. 07971

CEC Centron Educational Films, Centron Corp.
P.O. Box 687, Lawrence, KS 66044

CENCO Cenco Educational Films (Out of Business)
(Rent through university distribution center.)

CHUH Churchill Films
662 N. Robertson Blvd., Los Angeles, CA 90069

CORONET Coronet, Div. of Esquire, Inc.
65 E. South Water St., Chicago, IL 60601

DEGR Walter de Gruyter, Inc.
200 Sawmill River Rd., Hawthorne, N.Y. 10532

DOCA Document Associates, Inc.
573 Church Street, Toronto, Canada

EAL Ealing Film Loops
2225 Massachusetts Ave., Cambridge, MA 02140

EBEC	Encyclopedia Britannica Educational Corp. 425 N. Michigan Ave., Chicago, IL 60611
EDC	Educational Development Center 39 Chapel St., Newton, MA 02160
FA	Film Associates of California 11559 Santa Monica Blvd., Los Angeles, CA 90025
HFC	Handel Film Corporation 8730 Sunset Blvd., Los Angeles, CA 90069
HRW	Holt, Rinehart and Winston 383 Madison Ave., New York, NY 10017
IFB	International Film Bureau 332 South Michigan Ave., Chicago, IL 60604
INUAVC	Teaching Film Custodians (Order through Film Distribution Center, University of Indiana, Bloomington, IN 47405)
JF	Journal Films 930 Piner Ave., Evanston, IL 60202
KALMIA	Kalmia Company Dept. P-1, Concord, MA 01742
MCGH	Mcgraw-Hill Textfilms 330 W. 42nd St., New York, NY 10018
MIS	Moody Institute of Science 12000 E. Washington Blvd., Whittier, CA 90608
MLA	Modern Learning Aids P.O. Box 1712, Rochester, NY 14603
NASA	NASA Washington, DC 20546
NAVC	National Audio-Visual Center General Service Administration Reference Station, Washington, DC 20409
NCSU	North Carolina State University Raleigh, NC 27650

NTSU	North Texas State University, Department of Physics Denton, TX 76203
OHSU	Ohio State University 159 W. 19th Ave., Columbus, OH 43210
PERED	Perennial Education, Inc. 447 Roger Williams, Highland Park, IL 60035
PSU	Applied Research Laboratory Pennsylvania State University P.O. Box 30, State College, PA 16801
PURDUE	Purdue University Audio-Visual Center Rm. 54 Stew, Lafayette, IN 47097
PYRAMID	Pyramid Film Productions P.O. Box 1048, Santa Monica, CA 90406
RPI	Rensselear Polytechnic Institute Troy, NY 12181
SMITH	Steve Smith Associates 2341 Grant St., Berkely, CA 94703
STERLED	Sterling Educational Films, Inc. 241 E. 34th St., New York, NY 10016
TIME	Time-Life Films Multimedia Div. 100 Eisenhower Dr., Paramus, NJ 07652
UCMC	University of California Extension Media Center 2223 Fulton St., Berkely, CA 94720
UEVA	University Education and Visual Arts Div. of Universal City Studios, Inc. 100 Universal City Plaza, Universal City, CA 91608
UIAVC	University of Iowa Audio-Visual Center Media Library C-5 East Hall, Iowa City, IA 52242
USAEC	United States Atomic Energy Commission Division of Public Information Audio-Visual Branch, Washington, DC 20545

COMPUTERS

Computers are now making significant contributions to the teaching of physics. They are widely used in lectures to provide animated illustrations, with parameters under the control of the lecturer; they also provide tutorials and drills which students can work through on their own. The Physics Courseware Laboratory at the North Carolina State University (NCSU) maintains an up-to-date catalog of both commercial and public domain software, last published in *The Physics Teacher* of May, 1987. An international conference on Computers in Physics Instruction was held at NCSU in August 1988. Write to CPI Conference, Physics Department, NCSU, Raleigh NC 27695-8202 to order the following:

> *Computers in Physics Instruction: Software*. This consists of 34 computer teaching programs on 21 diskettes for 5 different computers (Macintosh, Amiga, IBM PC, Apple II, Commodore 64). $94/set.
>
> *Computers in Physics Instruction: Abstracts of Contributed Papers*, 238 pages, 122 papers. $16.50.

This instructor's resource manual for Cutnell/Johnson lists for various chapters of the text four types of computer exercises suitable for use by students in a College Physics course. Most **spreadsheet** references are on the **Teaching Aids** page of the appropriate chapter. The other three categories (**computer programs, computer projects, and interactive videodisk**) are listed under **Computer Resources** for each chapter. Each entry includes: name (or title), publisher (or supplier), computer, and a brief description. In addition there are several packages that cover large portions of the typical course called College Physics. Four widely available packages are:

PHYSICS I AND PHYSICS II SERIES (Control Data Company). Excellent problem solving tutorials for the IBM PC. Sixteen modules cover important topics in mechanics and 12 cover important topics in electrostatics, magnetostatics, and Faraday's law.

PHYSICS I (Microphysics Programs). A set of programs that generate problems covering particle dynamics and some aspects of thermodynamics. Different versions are available for IBM PC, Apple II, TRS-80 (models III and IV), Commodore Pet and 64.

PHYSICS SIMULATIONS (Kinko's). A great many demonstrations of important topics in introductory physics. Individual programs are listed for appropriate chapters in the **Computer Resources** section. These programs are for the Apple Macintosh.

SENSEI PHYSICS (Broderbund Software). Tutorial reviews with animated graphics of most of the major topics of introductory physics. Over 300 problems for student practice. These programs are for the Apple Macintosh.

You might consider setting aside a room or portion of a lab, equip it with several computers, and make tutorial, drill, and simulation programs available to students. If you have sufficient hardware (and software), you might base some assignments on computer materials.

Computers might also be used by students to perform calculations. Properly selected problems can add greatly to the students' understanding of physics. Problems involving the investigation of some physical system of interest might be assigned as individual projects or might be carried out in the laboratory.

Commercial spreadsheet programs, of the type used by business, can facilitate problem solving. For a detailed account of how they are used and a collection of informative problems, see *Wondering About Physics ... Using Spreadsheets to Find Out* by D.I. Dykstra and R.G. Fuller (John Wiley & Sons, 1988). Selections from this collection are listed in this instructor's resource manual under **Spreadsheets** on the **Teaching Aids** page for each chapter. Commercial problem solving programs such as *Eureka: The Solver* (Borland International) and *TK Solver!* (Universal Technical Systems Inc.) can easily be used by students to solve problems and graph results. In many cases, data generated by spreadsheets can also be imported to graph drawing programs. All these programs allow students to set up a problem generically, then view solutions for various values of input parameters. For example, the range or maximum height of a projectile can be found as a function of initial speed or firing angle, even if air resistance is taken into account.

KEY TO COMPUTER RESOURCES

Addison-Wesley Publishing Company
Reading, MA 01867

Borland International (Eureka!)
4585 Scotts Valley Drive, Scotts Valley, CA 95066

Cambridge Development Laboratory
1696 Massachusetts Avenue, Cambridge, MA 02138

Conduit, The University of Iowa, Oakdale Campus
Iowa City, IA 52242

Control Data Corporation
3601 West 77th Street, Bloomington, MN 55435

Cross Educational Software
P.O. Box 1536, Ruston, LA 71270

Mark Davids
21825 O'Conner, St. Clair Shores, MI 48080

Educational Materials and Equipment Company
P.O. Box 17
Pelham, NY 10803

EduTech
634 Commonwealth Avenue, Newton Center, Ma 02159

Focus Media, Inc.
839 Stewart Avenue, Garden City, NY 11530

R.H. Good, Physics Department
California State University at Hayward, CA 94542

High Technology Software Products
P.O. Box 60406, 1611 NW 23rd Street, Oklahoma City, OK 73146

HRM Software
175 Tompkins Avenue, Pleasantville, NY 10570-9973

J&S Software
140 Reed Avenue, Port Washington, NY 11050

Kinko's Service Corporation
4141 State Street, Santa Barbara, CA 93110

Merlan Scientific Ltd.
247 Armstrong Ave, Georgetown, Ontario L7G 4X6, Canada

Microphysics Programs
1737 West 2nd Street, Brooklyn, NY 11223

Norwalk High School, Science Department
County Street, Norwalk, CT 06851

Programs for Learning, Inc.
P.O. Box 954, New Milford, CT 06776

6502 Program Exchange
2920 Moana, Reno, NV 89509

Vernier Software
2920 89th Street, Portland, OR 97225

John Wiley & Sons, Inc., College Division
605 Third Avenue, New York, NY 10158-6088

SUGGESTED COURSES AND SAMPLE SCHEDULES

Like almost all books written for the college physics course that assumes a knowledge of algebra and some trigonometry, *Physics* by **John D. Cutnell and Kenneth W. Johnson** contains more material than can be covered in detail in a one-year course. We have in mind the typical course that carries 8 semester hours (or 12 quarter hours) credit. Most courses have a laboratory that students take concurrently. The book can be used equally well with a course that does not have a laboratory. In this case, however, the amount of material that can be covered in class will be somewhat less because, presumably, the laboratory experience will help students learn some of the material outside class.

We have prepared suggested schedules for a two-semester course and for a three-quarter course. We assumed that the class meets for three hours (50 minute hours) of lecture per week for 14 weeks each semester and for two-thirds of this (i.e., for about 10 weeks each quarter) if on the quarter system. Thus the schedules are based on 42 class meetings per semester (or 28 class meetings per quarter). Please note that we assumed that the course does not have a recitation meeting. We assumed that the first class of each term is devoted to orientation and the last class to review. We allowed for three tests during each semester and two during each quarter. This leaves 37 lectures per semester in which to cover the material. For the quarter system, we felt that a full orientation day would not be needed each quarter and that the review session at the end of the quarter would be somewhat less than a full class period. Thus we assumed 25 lectures available per quarter for covering the material in the book. We did not allow class time for a final examination because this is usually built into the college calendar.

The large number of topics in the textbook allows the instructor flexibility in choosing material pertinent to the needs of his/her class. The text can be easily adapted to serve the needs of a variety of student majors. The material that will be emphasized in a particular course depends on the approach used by the instructor. Thus the suggested schedules we have prepared include all chapters of the book. We did assume that the sections marked by an asterisk (*) in the book would not be covered in class, at least not in detail. The time allocated to each chapter is usually not sufficient to permit detailed coverage of all material in that chapter. Thus instructors will need to choose which sections will be omitted or covered only cursorialy. It is possible, of course, to omit entire chapters if the emphasis of the course is on detailed coverage of a limited number of topics. We felt, however, that the suggested schedules should include material from each chapter because many students (e.g., premedical students) often need a broad coverage to prepare for MCAT and similar professional type examinations. The suggested schedules are sufficiently flexible and complete that they should serve as a basis on which each instructor can construct a more detailed schedule to serve the needs of his/her students.

SUGGESTED SCHEDULE: TWO-SEMESTER COURSE

First Semester			Second Semester		
Text Chapter	Number of Lectures	Cumulative Lectures	Text Chapter	Number of Lectures	Cumulative Lectures
1	2.0	2.0	23	2.8	2.8
2	2.3	4.3	24	2.4	5.2
3	1.7	6.0	25	1.7	6.9
4	1.2	7.2	26	2.5	9.4
5	2.5	9.7	27	3.5	12.9
6	1.5	11.2	28	3.5	16.4
7	2.2	13.4	29	2.3	18.7
8	1.3	14.7	30	1.8	20.5
9	1.3	16.0	31	1.5	22.0
10	2.5	18.5	32	2.7	24.7
11	2.2	20.7	33	2.0	26.7
12	1.6	22.3	34	2.6	29.3
13	1.4	23.7	35	1.5	30.8
14	1.3	25.0	36	1.2	32.0
15	1.5	26.5	37	2.0	34.0
16	1.4	27.9	38	1.5	35.5
17	1.5	29.4	39	1.5	37.0
18	1.4	30.8			
19	1.7	32.5			
20	0.8	33.3			
21	1.9	35.2			
22	1.8	37.0			

SUGGESTED SCHEDULE: THREE-QUARTER COURSE

First Quarter			Second Quarter		
Text Chapter	Number of Lectures	Cumulative Lectures	Text Chapter	Number of Lectures	Cumulative Lectures
1	2.1	2.1	14	1.4	1.4
2	2.4	4.5	15	1.6	3.0
3	1.8	6.3	16	1.5	4.5
4	1.3	7.6	17	1.6	6.1
5	2.6	10.2	18	1.5	7.6
6	1.6	11.8	19	1.8	9.4
7	2.3	14.1	20	0.9	10.3
8	1.4	15.5	21	2.0	12.3
9	1.4	16.9	22	1.9	14.2
10	2.6	19.5	31	1.6	15.8
11	2.3	21.8	32	2.8	18.6
12	1.7	23.5	33	2.1	20.7
13	1.5	25.0	34	2.7	23.4
			35	1.6	25.0

Third Quarter

Text Chapter	Number of Lectures	Cumulative Lectures
23	2.7	2.7
24	2.3	5.0
25	1.6	6.6
26	2.4	9.0
27	3.4	12.4
28	3.4	15.8
29	2.2	18.0
30	1.7	19.7
36	1.0	20.7
37	1.8	22.5
38	1.3	23.8
39	1.2	25.0

IDEAS FOR THE FIRST TIME LECTURER

ABSTRACT

Aspiring middle-aged professor of physics, A.B. in English (Phi Beta Kappa), Ph.D. in Physics (Sigma Xi), 31 years experience in quality institutions (College of William and Mary, Oak Ridge National Laboratory, and Old Dominion University), seeks opportunity to converse with inspiring young assistant professors of physics for the purpose of exploring the art of teaching our favorite subject to today's students.

HOW I GOT HERE

A few months ago, in a moment of either great weakness or deceptive anticipation, I agreed to write a few pages of comments that might be helpful to some newly minted, academically certified, moderately ambitious assistant professor of physics. Ever since that ill-fated moment, I've been racking my brain in an effort to extract some nuggets of wisdom to share with the first time lecturer. But the ideas that sounded so profound and brilliant when discussed informally with colleagues over the years seemed to have lost their luster when I tried to put them in writing. Of course, I shouldn't really be surprised by this; it's certainly not the first time I've been surprised as a teacher. This leads me to suggest that the first time lecturer would do well to get used to surprises. Let me mention a few that I, and most of the physics professors I know, have encountered along the way.

THREE SURPRISES I'VE ENCOUNTERED

My first full-time college appointment was in the fall of 1958. This was the first academic year following the launching of Sputnik some eleven months earlier. The fairly prestigious college that took a chance on me had very good students and, because of the space race with its emphasis on science, a goodly number of these students enrolled in physics. They were bright; I was a novice. The interaction of the bright and eager students with the inexperienced but determined teacher led the latter to his first surprise which, in reality, is a closely related pair of surprises.

THE FIRST SURPRISE: I remember being surprised at how quickly the students learned at first, at how rapidly they absorbed (and, I thought, even mastered) the material as I led them through translational kinematics and dynamics. I distinctly remember a feeling of trepidation that at this rate of learning these students' knowledge of physics would soon surpass mine, at which time I wouldn't even be able to keep a chapter ahead of them. And then about midsemester I noticed that most of them no longer learned the material at first glance; indeed some even had to struggle almost as much as I had some years previously in a similar university physics course. I had to go more slowly, to discuss principles from several perspectives, to give more examples than previously. Much to my surprise, the class that initially had learned so effortlessly now labored to understand linear momentum and kinetic energy. What joy I felt in joining faculty colleagues, even occasionally senior ones, in bemoaning the sad state of today's students as we longed for scholars who were as eager and talented as we had been. But in more reflective moments I began to realize that the students were still bright--it was just that they had reached a learning plateau with the result that a considerable incubation period was needed to absorb new concepts and, especially, to correlate these with principles previously ingested. Gradually I began to understand that a tightly-structured, sequential discipline such as physics--particularly Newtonian mechanics--requires a rather extensive incubation period. It's so easy (not to mention convenient) for seasoned physicists and accomplished teachers to forget the inordinate amount of time we spent (we thought it was wasted) in making false starts, going down blind alleys, and pursuing wayward detours before we managed to integrate different aspects of physics into a meaningful pattern that enabled us to appreciate, or even to see, the forest rather than experience bewilderment as we stared at the multiplicity of trees. While I still try to adhere to high standards for student performance, I try to be more patient if they don't immediately comprehend all of the subtleties.

THE SECOND SURPRISE: Another surprise is how little interest most students in my introductory courses have in physics. Why don't they share my enthusiasm for the topic under discussion? Why do they spend as little time on physics as they can get by with? I asked them to look at some questions and problems at the end of the kinematics chapter--and then when I tried to hold a discussion in class, it was soon evident that most of them didn't get around to the assignment. Well, to be honest, as a student I myself very seldom got around to college assignments that were not to be turned in. It wasn't that I was uninterested or totally lazy. It's just that I was so busy doing homework for those courses in which assignments were collected that I had no time left for optional academic pursuits. It's amazing how little time students (and indeed most of us) have for those activities that are optional and how much time we can find for activities that are required. As one of my Navy friends put it, *"You get what you inspect, not what you expect."* So I insist that my students hand in a homework assignment once a week. Subsequently I'll discuss homework assignments and grading in more detail.

THE THIRD SURPRISE: This last surprise pertains not to students--but to me. When I first became a faculty member, I was surprised at how much time teaching a physics course took. As a graduate student I had done some teaching that, although demanding, had not required nearly as much time as when I became a faculty member. Gradually I realized that there is a difference between being an assistant who serves a limited role in a course and being a faculty member who assumes full responsibility for the viability of the entire course--the lecture, the laboratory, the recitation, the tests, and perhaps most important, the students. I was also surprised that so little time was available for preparing for class--there always seemed to be committees, visitors, students, reports required by the administration, a proposal to write, a research project to help with, etc. Somehow one has to learn to budget one's time and to invest it wisely--not that I've been very effective at this.

So much for three surprises--three among many. Let me now discuss the rationale for the lecture system; after this I will make some suggestions regarding skills and techniques that may be helpful in lecturing.

IS THE LECTURE SYSTEM HERE TO STAY?

Yes, it is. At least I think it is. You know why? Well, as I tell my students, a lecture has been aptly defined as an ingenious device by which information in the instructor's notes is transferred to the student's notes without passing through the heads of either. The student is willing to pay tuition (i.e., money) for the privilege and pleasure of participating in this system and the professoriate gets paid, some rather handsomely, for services rendered. Now who is going to agitate to abolish such an arrangement? Viewed from another perspective, the lecture has been around a long time and doubtless has survived onslaughts from administrators who want to be more cost efficient and from various and sundry other constituencies. But the system has survived, even thrived. Surely such a long-lived system must be serving some societal, and perhaps even educational, purpose. Of course, I readily admit that the lecture is a very expensive and inefficient method of transmitting information. Once, as a naive idealist, I informed my class that the lecture really should have been abolished shortly after the invention of the printing press--and that henceforth I would expect them to become conversant with the factual material in the textbook on their own and that time in class would be used to answer any questions they might have, to explain any ambiguities in the text, and most importantly to explore through mutual discussion the subtleties and implications of the facts--with me serving as a resource person, moderator, and mentor (like Socrates, you know). This novelty lasted almost a couple of days, whereupon we settled again into the tried and proven (or at least accepted) lecture system. The imminent departure of the lecture has been repeatedly forecast since at least the mid-1700's, as witness Boswell's quoting [1] Dr. Samuel Johnson as saying:

"Lectures were once useful; but now, when all can read, and books are so numerous, lectures are unnecessary. If your attention fails, and you miss part of the lecture, it is lost; you cannot go back as you do upon a book."

(Have I not read virtually these same words within the last year except that the word **books** was replaced by **computers**?) Despite such dire prognostications, statements regarding the death of the lecture system--like statements pertaining to the demise of Mark Twain-- have been grossly exaggerated. I will return later to the lecture system and speak positively about some of its strengths. I merely wanted in this present section to establish some basis to support the view that the lecture system is here to stay and that, therefore, it is worthwhile for the beginning physics teacher to acquire some skills and techniques that experienced lecturers have found useful. We turn now to this task.

THE SINE QUA NON FOR GOOD LECTURERS

Before considering specific skills and strategies that successful physics lecturers have found useful, I want to make some general comments regarding the overall approach to being a good teacher of introductory physics. Let me first set forth what I perceive to be our ultimate objective. I can do no better than to cite[2] the "Report of Conferences on the Improvement of College Teaching" and to say that I agree with the distinguished physics professors (Francis Bitter, Francis L. Friedman, Walter C. Michels, Francis W. Sears, Frank Verbrugge, and Jerrold R. Zacharias) who prepared the report in 1960. They state:

"The overall aim of college physics teaching is the same as that of all higher education: to help students think and act in ways appropriate to the modern world."

Note that our goal is to *"help students think and act."* Every word here is significant. We are to **help.** We can no more do the thinking and acting for the student than we can digest his food. We cannot grow, we cannot study, we cannot learn for the student. In fact, we cannot do anything for a person that a person **must** do for himself; we can only help. But note that we physicists do not have to do all of the helping. While I contend that, even among the sciences, physics has something unique to contribute, let us be aware that other professors, other disciplines, other college experiences will do part of the helping. Of the four key words in the phrase quoted above, two (**think** and **act**) will be addressed in a subsequent section. The fourth key word, **students**, has a central role in the following section in which I discuss four facets of knowledge that are essential (i.e., *sine qua non*) for the first time lecturer, the last time lecturer, and all other lecturers anywhere in between on the road from beginning to retiring.

FOUR THINGS YOU MUST KNOW

First, and by far the most important, **KNOW YOUR SUBJECT**. There is no way at all that we teach college physics so as to "*help students think and act ... in ways appropriate to the modern world*" if we do not know our discipline, our physics. I do not propose to say anything further on this topic because I trust that the college that appointed this newly minted, first time lecturer assured itself that he/she met this primary qualification. I would note, however, that knowing a subject and teaching the subject are different. As I prepare for my classes, I try not only to refresh my knowledge of the physics to be covered but also to think back to long ago days when I was learning this part of physics. I find it helpful to recall the difficulties I had in understanding these particular concepts. In short, I try to become a beginner again so that I can anticipate the difficulties my students will encounter as they try to follow the concepts I'm trying to help them learn. This brings me to the second essential thing a first time lecturer needs to know.

Second, **KNOW YOUR STUDENTS**. I went into teaching physics because I wanted to teach physics. But it didn't take very long to realize that while it doubtless would be nice to **teach physics**, that option was not available to me. Why not? Well, simply because my assignment was to **teach physics to students** -- and that was much more difficult but also ultimately much more rewarding. We need to know something about how students learn (i.e., the cognitive process), about the emotional and intellectual development of young persons just entering college, about the tensions they experience in daily living, about how to motivate them, about the demands that disciplines other than physics place on them. Rather than expounding at length on our need to be conversant with matters of this type, I will forthwith summon an expert witness who will establish beyond reasonable doubt that we need to know our students. The witness is Robert A. Millikan, recipient in 1940 of the Oersted Medal awarded by the American Association of Physics teachers for "notable contributions to the teaching of physics." Here[3] is his testimony:

> "*The most important job of the teacher is to know his students, every one of them, so that he will make few mistakes as possible in rating their qualities and their capacities justly and accurately in order that he may steer them wisely. Talking entertainingly to a hundred or two hundred students is a wholly subordinate and trivial requirement of a good teacher. The great, indispensable requisite is conscientiousness in watching carefully and discriminatingly the way his students solve problems, the way they do their laboratory work, the way they answer questions, the way they pose questions of their own. This job cannot be delegated to anyone else without abdicating the main job of the teacher.*"

Knowing your students also implies knowing your class as an entity. This means knowing their capacity, their intellectual potential, their present knowledge of the subject. Knowing these abilities will help you to avoid both dwelling overly long on the obvious (and thereby boring most of the class) and spending too much time on the incomprehensible (and thereby losing almost everyone).

Knowing the persons on one side of the lecture desk will not result in effective teaching unless you also know the human on the opposite of the desk. Thus the third essential component is: **KNOW YOURSELF.** As has already been mentioned, without a doubt you know your subject. It is almost equally certain that you know yourself fairly well. You rose to the challenge of earning a Ph.D. in Physics and, perhaps after serving a postdoctoral, you found a college position. Thus you must be intelligent, resourceful, and persistent; these will stand you in good stead as you begin teaching full time. While pursuing your doctorate, you probably served a year or two as a graduate teaching assistant and thereby acquired experience in supervising a laboratory, teaching a recitation section, grading homework, and perhaps even lecturing to introductory classes once in a while. Now that you are among the professoriate, you will need to know yourself even better. Is college teaching really your cup of tea? How will you apportion your time among competing demands of research, teaching, committee work, and service to the college, to professional organizations, and to the community in which you live? Be assured that a nearby school will invite you to speak to their science club and/or to judge a science fair. All of these involvements take time and any one of them could consume almost all of your time (as well as your energy and creative drive) if you let it. Allocation of your time to various endeavors is something you must decide. Talk to faculty colleagues--young ones like yourself, those somewhat older who have recently achieved tenure, and older ones who've survived in *la academe*. Determine what the reward structure at your institution is--and meet the requirements of that structure or seek your fortune elsewhere.

Each new assistant professor has different talents to offer and each has different priorities. But I strongly urge everyone to **stay involved in research and to be an effective teacher.** I would try **to achieve excellence either in research or in teaching** and to make at least a modest contribution in the other. I tend toward the view that the major thrust of your work during the first few years should be toward getting a research program established on campus. If you are at an institution that offers graduate degrees in physics, you almost certainly will need to be active in research to have any chance of getting tenure. Effective teaching is essential also--but good teaching alone usually will not lead to tenure. There are, of course, many different types of institutions, and what holds at a university may not have the same priority at a liberal arts college or a community college. In any event, even if one has a situation in which involvement in physics research is nearly impossible, all of us should be engaged in some type of scholarly activity beyond the classroom. The point of this section is that you need to know your abilities, your interests, your goals, and your own limitations--and allocate your time and effort accordingly, realizing that you cannot be all things to all students, all committees, all research involvements. You must learn to focus your efforts, or you will be perceived as reasonably effective in many areas but with no distinctive excellence in any one area--in other words, jack of all trades and master of none. And this, for an untenured assistant professor, usually leads to a dead end. A dead end leads nowhere--but the end of this paragraph leads to the fourth thing you must know.

KNOW YOUR PEDAGOGY. At least know enough about pedagogy to be aware of simple skills and techniques that have helped physics professors (and others too) to become competent in the craft of teaching. In this context we are interested in applied pedagogy, in those tricks of the trade that are directly and immediately useful to the first time lecturer--so instead of becoming philosophical in discussing this fourth essential, I will terminate this present section and get down to brass ticks in the next.

HOW TO LECTURE: SKILLS AND TECHNIQUES

How much of your lecture should be devoted to going over material covered in the text? How closely should you stick to the text? Should you use lecture notes? What kind? Should you rehearse your lecture beforehand? Is is best to use a microphone in lecturing to large classes? How should one handle students who want to talk in class? Is it worthwhile to assign homework? How much homework? Is grading homework and tests very time consuming? These "nuts and bolts" items will be addressed in this section. Let me note that the guideline established for me by the John Wiley Physics Editor is that this section should be "what an experienced/successful College Physics instructor would relate to a colleague teaching the course for the first time." I make no claim to being very successful, but I cannot deny that I've been around a long time and hence am experienced. Should a first time lecturer seek my counsel, I seriously doubt that I would give him/her a learned and tightly woven lecture. On the contrary, I probably would ramble a great deal and take excursions along side roads as the two of us talked about the "methods and materials" of teaching. This is the approach I'll use here--except that I'll record only my part of the dialogue.

AN INFORMAL CHAT WITH
A FIRST TIME LECTURER

I'll tell you about the things that work well for me. Others have found that a different style works best for them. You'll want to develop your own style--if you don't, you'll never enjoy teaching. I'm flattered that you came to me first to discuss teaching, but please be sure to talk with several others, especially to some of the younger, but still experienced, ones. You were asking about the **syllabus**. I myself use a one-page syllabus and am very suspicious about those who use more than four or five pages. I include the following:

Information about the course: the course number, the section number, the class meeting days and hours; information as appropriate on recitation (if any) and lab.

Information about myself: my name, room and phone numbers for my office, my office hours.

Materials for the course: I also indicate which items are required and which are optional. Typical materials are: textbook, lab manual, calculator, study guide, type of notebooks for lecture and for lab, ruler, graph paper, etc.

Information on testing and grading: I state the number of tests (I give three); some semesters I specify the dates for each test; other semesters I omit the dates and just state that tests will be announced at least one week in advance. I specify the relative weighting of each component (tests, exam, homework, lab, recitation) in determining the final grade in the course.

Information pertaining to homework: Format for submitting homework (kind of paper, how folded, etc); when assigned (I assign homework one week in advance of due date); due date; penalty for late homework; where to turn homework in (I use a hallway locker--I don't like the hassle of turning homework in in class and the confrontation that often ensues when a student turns his/hers in after class rather than at the beginning); state that I will respond (in class) to general inquiries regarding homework but not help students individually with homework; whether homework is pledged or not (I encourage my students to work together on homework and to get help from anyone other than me); when and where homework solutions will be posted or otherwise made available.

Classroom Management (Housekeeping): Are seats assigned? If so, how? (I let students choose where to sit in class; then I assign the seats accordingly. I assign different seats for tests.) Is roll taken? Is attendance required? Are make-up tests given? If so, on what basis? Can formula sheets be used on tests? Are some formulas given? How about constants?

In summary, I put on the syllabus the minimum essential information that I believe the student needs to know in order to participate in the course. Other, perhaps most, teachers use a longer syllabus that might include course objectives, list of chapters (or topics) to be covered and on what date, reading assignments, homework assignments and due dates, hints on studying, problem solving, etc. I would suggest: (1) following local guidelines and practices as to what should be put in the syllabus, (2) keeping the syllabus fairly short (two or three pages maximum), (3) making the syllabus functional rather than philosophical, (4) designing the syllabus to be useful to the student rather than as a massive document intended to impress some administrator, and (5) not wasting time and effort by having the department secretary copy into the syllabus the table of contents of the textbook.

AN ASIDE TO THE READER: In real time, the preceding two pages would have taken three or four minutes; I'd simply give the person copies of two or three syllabi used by me and make brief comments on them.

THE FIRST CLASS MEETING

You asked a moment ago if it's okay to include on the syllabus comments on matters such as: how I conduct the class, whether students can interrupt to ask questions, suggestions to students on how to study, taking notes and reading ahead. Certainly it's okay to include these items. In fact, it's okay to include anything you want to. My own approach is to discuss matters of this sort at the first class meeting rather than on the syllabus, but this is really a matter of taste or style. This first class meeting is very important; you know the old saying that first impressions are lasting. Let the class know what your approach to lecturing is. I tend to stick fairly close to the book in the ordering of topics. My lecture notes (such as they are) and the notes I write on the projector (or board) in class are built around the text. The faculty have selected what they consider to be a good text, and the students have paid dearly for the book, so I use the book as the scaffolding around which to teach the course. I do give additional examples, especially ones that involve pertinent current news events, such as the tragic earthquake in the Soviet Union (Armenia) that was on the front page of the newspaper the day I wrote these words. But back to the first day of class. I introduce myself, welcome them, hand out the syllabus--and then I go over the syllabus with them step by step. I let them ask questions. I try to come across as a real person. (Actually I don't try to; I want to and hope I do-- but I don't try to, because then I won't.) I make additional comments on my lecture style and the other items you asked about above. I tell them that this course will be demanding and that my expectations are high but reasonable and realistic. I let them know that I am available to help them outside class if they will take the initiative to come see me. And one other thing I try to do the first day; I try to cover some physics. Although it may be for only five minutes, I like to get the course started--and for them to realize that the course has started and that they also need to get started. So much for the syllabus and the first day of class. The ice has been broken; teacher and students have faced each other across the lecture table and both have survived. Now let's consider the next class; you'll have a full period to talk about physics then.

PROJECTORS AND BLACKBOARDS

Most physics teachers try to communicate with their students both orally and visually. That is, we talk (so students will hear the physics) and we write (so that they will see what we are talking about). Now there are some useful guidelines on using seeing and hearing effectively. In discussing the art of giving a lecture, George E. Uhlenbeck, co-discoverer of electron spin, recalls [4] the advice he and his fellow students received from their physics professor.

"I can still hear Ehrenfest exclaim in his typical mixture of German and Dutch when one of us students gave a talk: 'Please, start writing on the upper left-hand corner of the blackboard!; please, do not erase before people have a chance to see what you wrote; please, do not talk with your face to the blackboard,' etc. All perhaps rather trivial points but one has only to go to a meeting of the American Physical Society to see how often people sin against these rather simple rules."

This reminds me that you and I were chatting a couple of days ago about whether to use the blackboard or the overhead projector. My own preference is the projector because I am facing the class while writing. Thus I can talk to them (not to the board); I can also see them and observe their reactions. Also, I can write in rather small letters, yet students in the rear of a fairly large lecture room can still see the diagrams and notes I make. Some teachers prefer the blackboard. Paul G. Hewitt, of the City College of San Francisco, who is known far and wide as a superb teacher, uses the board. But whichever you use, be sure that what your writing is easily seen by students at the rear of the room. I also suggest that the diagrams you draw be clear, neat, and uncluttered. Just before you dropped by to chat, I was browsing through that new book we've adopted for our College Physics course--you know, the one by Cutnell and Johnson. One of the things I like about that book is that the drawings are elegantly simple and each figure concentrates on a single main idea. One picture is worth a thousand words--but only if the picture is focused.

One reason I prefer the overhead projector to the blackboard is that it's easier for me to make good drawings on the acetate. Another reason is that I can prepare drawings beforehand and bring them to class. This is especially desirable when the figure needs to drawn carefully and to scale rather than just being a rough sketch. As you know, our department has a photocopying machine that will make transparencies and will enlarge and reduce the size. This makes it fairly easy to make a transparency of any figure in the text and indeed from other books and journals. Lastly, I find that I can use different colors easily and effectively with the projector. You've probably heard other faculty members here remark that I'm not one to use a fancy, multicolored, precisely drawn transparency when a simple sketch is just as effective if not more so. Please let me caution you about using different colors to excess. Use colors to highlight the central ideas and to give some variety, but indiscriminate use of color to dazzle the student or just to make a cute drawing seems to me to be counterproductive.

I like the quote above in which Professor Ehrenfest urged that speakers "...*not erase before people have a chance to see what you wrote.*" I remember that in college we used to kid about old Professor X who wrote on the board with his right hand and immediately erased the writing with an eraser held in his left hand so that at any given instant the board contained only about three feet of writing, and Professor X stood directly in front of that. This is one of the difficulties with both the board and the projector--it's so easy to stand in front of the writing. Many instructors find it helpful to pause every few minutes, to step aside from the board or projector, and to wait for students to catch up. While at first the silence seems awkward, the change of pace may recapture the attention of some students who have been daydreaming about...about...well, let's just say they were daydreaming about something other than physics. This business of the mind wandering away from the subject being discussed leads me to make a few comments regarding the **attention span**.

THE ATTENTION SPAN

When my children were small, they enjoyed watching the Saturday morning cartoons on television. You probably watched them yourself. Did you ever notice how short a given segment of a TV program (cartoon or otherwise) is before they switch to something different (and not necessarily just to another commercial). Take a look sometimes at some of the popular and highly rated children's educational programs such as Sesame Street or Newton's Apple. It often seems that they hardly get into a scene before they switch to another topic. Yet it's rather widely agreed that these programs are effective. Of course, the reason behind this frequent switching from one topic to another is the fact that children can concentrate on one idea for only a short time; after that the mind wanders. In other words, children have an **attention span** of a few minutes. But so do college students, at least the ones who are in my classes. I'm amazed by the scheduling of some college classes. For example, I know of a graduate level course that's scheduled from 6:00 p.m. to 9:45 p.m. with only one 10 minute break included. People put in a full day at work, grab a bite to eat, fight rush hour traffic to get to the college, and sit for four hours with only a 10 minute break! Whoever scheduled this may be able to count minutes of class time needed to get 3 semester hours credit, but I don't think they are aware that the mind can absorb no more than the seat can endure. For a graphic demonstration of the attention span, may I suggest that you attend a physics seminar, preferably one held just after lunch. Even though it's a topic in which you are interested, and even though the speaker is pretty good, notice how quickly the mind wanders and you feel inclined to doze off. This is especially true if, like the students in most college physics classes, you aren't able to follow the chain of development being presented.

It behooves all of us, whether first time lecturer or seasoned veteran, to be aware of the attention span and to have frequent changes of pace in our presentations. Some possibilities are: covering a concept and then presenting an example or two (going from the abstract to the concrete); taking a few minutes of class time and letting the students become actively involved by working an example themselves; using variety in our speaking pattern--varying the cadence a bit (e.g., using a slow cadence when we talk about a slowly moving train); varying the loudness with which we speak (talk in a whisper when you're explaining low decibel sounds); interspersing demonstrations throughout the class period; using a short film loop to vary the pace; providing the class with frequent breathing spaces (I've already mentioned stepping aside from the projector and waiting a minute or so for students to catch up); using gestures and a variety thereof; doing a bit of acting (e.g., if you're discussing translational, rotational, and vibrational degrees of freedom of molecules, pretend you're a water molecule with your head as **O** and your fists as **H's** and ham it up a bit; years later remember their half-witted professor, and they'll recall at least a little bit of physics along with the acting); providing the opportunity for questions or perhaps for comments; giving a pop quiz (guaranteed to get their attention); looking at different sections of the audience; trying to establish eye contact; pausing abruptly and waiting patiently while two students stop whispering to each other; using a bit of humor once in a while; making reference to current events or to persons in the news (I'm currently on a "Read my lips" kick--but one has to be very careful with matters bordering on politics or religion--also on sex). I could go on and on--like most professors, I'm very likely to keep going on and on--but I believe you get the idea. The important thing is to develop your own style; talk to others to get ideas but adapt them to your own talents and needs.

ORGANIZATION OF THE LECTURE

It may be helpful to talk a bit about organization of the lecture. Should one have detailed lecture notes? Should the lecture be tightly woven and somewhat formal? Should you repeat the key parts of the lecture so that those who didn't understand it the first time will have a chance to catch up? There are many approaches to organizing and presenting a lecture. One of the best I know is reputed to have come from a man who, though he had little formal education, has acquired a local reputation as an effective speaker. He explained his approach in simple terms:

"First I tell 'em what I'm gonna tell 'em.
Then I tell 'em.
Then I tell 'em what I told em."

From my experience as a physics teacher, I would add:

"Then if you're lucky,
Half of the time,
Half of the class will remember
Half of what you said...if you tell 'em again."

Often in our teaching we rush directly into a concept without giving the student a preliminary view of where we are headed and why. One of the things I noticed about Cutnell and Johnson is that they briefly explain the purpose of an upcoming example to help the student see the development in perspective. But we don't want to spend the whole class period telling the student what we are going to do.. Better to give a brief overview and then proceed with the development. In doing so, it is important to speak to the student in terms that are meaningful to him/her. Just this morning an article in the local newspaper called attention to this in connection with a story in a basic reader being used by students at an inner city school. One of the teachers noted that the story was "*about a tractor factory in the midwest. Lots of our kids have never seen* a tractor before and don't know how it works. They can't relate to the story." When I was a youngster, all the children in my hometown knew that cream rose to the top of the bottle of unhomogenized milk; we had seen this many times. We understood when out science teacher used this experience in discussing density. Today's students have never seen cream rise to the top and generally do not know that cream is less dense than milk. It's not that they are ignorant or unobservant; it's just that they have different experiences. If the topic deals with projectile motion, students will perk up if the instructor illustrates time of flight by referring to the hang time of a football punt. In talking about momentum and impulse, it's helpful to call attention to a bat striking a baseball. We sometimes get so carried away with using esoteric examples as illustrations of physical laws that we overlook phenomena that students encounter every day. As Paul Hewitt remarked: [5]

> *"I feel uneasy about such things as students examining the photographs of bubble-chamber tracks when they don't understand bubbles in a carbonated drink or in boiling water."*

As for "telling 'em what you told 'em," it is advisable to review from time to time so that the class can view the development in hindsight. For example, when discussing rotational motion, first in terms of kinematics and then of dynamics, remind the students of the parallel path pursued in discussing translational motion. This helps them to assimilate the various concepts into a coherent pattern.

HOMEWORK, TESTS, AND GRADES

When I was discussing the syllabus with you, I indicated that I would make further comments regarding homework. I believe that it is essential to assign homework at least once a week and that it be collected and graded. Use as many techniques (such as homework) as you can to get students to participate actively in the course. Arnold B. Arons, a physics professor who has played a leading role in research on the learning process, noted: [6]

> *".. the widely prevalent illusion that students will master concepts, theories, and arts of thinking and reasoning through inculcation, i.e., by reading or by passive listening to sufficiently lucid expositions. This is demonstrably not the case. Activity must be induced within the intellect of each individual student."*

How much homework should one assign? There obviously are different practices here. My approach is to assign three problems of moderate difficulty each week. An undergraduate student grades all problems, but not in detail that is used in grading tests. (I grade the tests.) We grade the homework generously. Each problem is graded on a 10-point scale and deductions are made in half-point increments. I have found that students are much happier to have 0.5 of a point deducted on a 10-point scale than to lose 5 points on a 100-point scale. Although the proportions are the same in the two cases, student perception and reaction are different. This method saves me considerable time in discussing with individual students the grade on their homework. Rather than grading every assigned problem, some instructors count the number of problems solved and then grade one randomly selected problem in detail. I know of one large university in which homework problems are assigned with answers given in a multiple choice format, the primary reason being not to save time in grading but to avoid arguing with students about how much credit was given. Whatever grading scheme is used, I urge that homework be collected. In preparing hour tests for your class, ask your colleagues to give you samples from previous years. I try to return tests, especially the first test each semester, to the students as promptly as possible. Regarding a reasonable distribution of final grades in the course, I suggest that you talk with other faculty who have taught the same course and know what the pattern is at you college.

DON'T TRY TO COVER THE WHOLE TEXTBOOK

One of the pitfalls of which all of us should be wary is that of rushing pell mell through the book whether students are with us or not. You may have heard the story about the professor who moved so fast through the book that when a student dropped his pencil, he got two chapters behind before he could pick it up. We are tempted to be comprehensive in our coverage, to give students an exposure to every topic discussed in the text. This is a treadmill that leads to frustration for both the student and teacher. As was noted [7] in the 1960 report previously cited:

> *"We do well to realize that when we go too fast, or shoot over the heads of our students, we are likely to create frustration, bewilderment, and a loss of the self-confidence so essential to disciplined thinking."*

Textbooks tend to be encyclopedic in their coverage of topics. This rather comprehensive coverage allows flexibility and makes the book suitable for a broad range of courses that have slightly different emphases. The authors and publishers of the book have little expectation that all of the book will be covered in any one course. Trying to do so leads us into the trap cited by Clifford E. Swartz in an editorial [8] titled *"Too much, too fast, too soon."* As an old saying puts it: *How much physics we cover is less important than how physics we uncover.* As noted by Philip Morrison in his classic lecture [9] *"Less may be more,"* covering fewer topics may result in teaching more physics. The decision on how much to cover is intimately related to the more fundamental decision as to what we want an introductory physics course to accomplish. Do we want to communicate just the factual content or do we also want our students to understand the process by which the facts came to be known?

If we wish to explain as well as inform, we will have to limit coverage. As Arnold Arons put it: [10]

> "*There is, it seems to me, no alternative to slowing up, cutting off some of the desperate coverage, even if it is as painful as cutting off a finger or an arm, and giving the students a chance to focus some attention on the process in which knowledge and understanding of a new concept are acquired.*"

SOME CONCLUDING REMARKS

I hope you choose a good text for your course; many fine ones are available. But remember that you, not the book, should be the anchor of the course. To many students, the printed word is almost sacred; the text is the final authority. Anthony P. French tells of an incident that occurred in a course in which the text was one of the books he had written. He writes: [11]

> "*...at the end of one lecture a student came up to me with a question, pointed to a page in the book, and said,'He says here that...' without the slightest awareness that the 'he' was myself!*"

I have attempted in these pages to set down some guidelines that may be helpful to the first time lecturer. Some contend that teachers are born, not made. In discussing this "born not made" attitude, Eble [12] compares teachers and athletes. He notes that great athletes are certainly born with potential abilities but that they must develop these through practice. He writes:

> "*Potentially great teachers become great teachers by the same route: through conditioning mind and spirit and body, acquiring skills and practicing in respectful competition with great teachers, living and dead.*"

I hope that you will be diligent in mastering these skills, in conditioning yourself, in practicing, even in rehearsing. But remember that good teaching is more than the application of pedagogical techniques. Good teaching is an interaction between student and teacher, a meeting of personalities, a communication of minds. I am reminded in this connection of a comment made by the great pianist, Arthur Rubenstein, when asked to explain the difference between himself and Mr. X, a technically superb pianist who seldom struck a wrong note but did not electrify an audience as did Rubinstein, who hit wrong notes more frequently.

Rubinstein answered [13] in effect:

> *"Both Mr. X and I are talented. When we are preparing for a concert, both of us practice diligently day after day. The only difference is that when concert time arrives, I go stage and make music for the audience whereas Mr. X goes on stage and practices some more."*

Most of us are run-of-the mill physicists who will be only moderately effective teachers. But no matter whether we are outstanding or merely competent, let us at least go into the classroom and teach physics, not rehearse some more pedagogical techniques. Let us communicate the spirit and excitement of our discipline. Enjoy your year as a first time lecturer!

REFERENCES

1. G.B. Hill, ed. *Boswell's Life of Johnson,* revised and enlarged edition by L. F. Powell (Oxford, 1934), Vol. IV, p. 92.

2. *American Journal of Physics 28* , 568 (1960).

3. Robert A. Millikan, *American Journal of Physics 9* , 82 (1941).

4. G. E. Uhlenbeck, *American Journal of Physics 24* , 431 (1956).

5. Paul G. Hewitt, *The Physics Teacher 10* , 522 (1972).

6. A. B. Arons, *AAPT Pathways* (American Association of Physics Teachers, College Park, MD, 1981), p. 10.

7. *American Journal of Physics 28* , 573 (1960).

8. Cliff Swartz, *The Physics Teacher 18* ; 258 (1980).

9. Phillip Morrison, *American Journal Of Physics 32* , 441 (1964).

10. Arnold Arons, *The Physics Teacher 6* , 339 (1968).

11. A. P. French, *American Journal of Physics 56* , 111 (1988).

12. Kenneth E. Eble, *The Craft of Teaching* (Jossey-Bass, San Francisco, 1977), p. 17.

13. *TIME*, February 25, 1966, p. 85.

CHAPTER 1: TEACHING AIDS
INTRODUCTION AND MATHEMATICAL CONCEPTS

Transparencies:
Figure 1.11: The standard platinum-iridium meter bar.
Figure 1.14: The vector A and its components, A_x and A_y.

Solved Problems:
Text Problem 39 is Study Guide Example 3.

Spreadsheets:
#01: Reaction Time
#02: Airplane Flight Times

Demonstrations:
Measurements: Freier and Anderson Ma-1 - 3;
Hilton M-1
Vectors: Freier and Anderson Mb-2, 3;
Hilton M-10;
Meiners 6-4.7, 6-4.8, 6-4.9

1. Body Language: Help students to develop a feel for metric units by noting the sizes of various parts of the human body. The fingernail of the little finger is about 1 cm wide; a 6'7" basketball player is 2 m tall. Ask students to calculate their mass in kg.

2. Volume: Fill a 1-quart bottle with water and pour the water into a l liter pop bottle to show that a liter is larger than a quart. Have students calculate the price per gallon of gasoline when the cost per liter is given. Similarly, have them express a speed in mi/h and in km/h.

3. Time: To give students a feel for time intervals, ask students to keep their eyes closed for 1 minute beginning at the instant you start a large stopclock at the front of the room. Most students considerably underestimate the duration of a minute. When I tried this once with a class, one student went to sleep and kept her eyes shut for the rest of the hour.

Films:
Meters, Liters, and Kilograms, 16mm, color, 23 min., PERED
Time and Clocks (PSSC), 16mm, b/w, 28 min., MLA
Powers of Ten (Eames), 16mm or 3/4" videocassette, b/w, 10 min. or 25 min.,
Pyramid

Laboratory:
Bernard and Epp: #1: Determination of Length, Mass, and Density
Preston: #1: Simple Pendulum (Empirical Equations)

Computer Resources for Chapter 1

Programs:

1. *Vector Addition II*. Vernier. Apple II. User supplies magnitude and direction of up to 19 vectors. Individual vectors and their resultant are drawn on the monitor screen and the magnitude and direction of the resultant are given numerically. Handy for lectures; also good to drill students. Reviewed TPT February 1986.

2. *College Physics Series, Vol. I: Vectors and Graphics*. Cross. Apple II+. Tutorials on the resolution of vectors into components, vector addition. scalar product, vector product. Reviewed TPT January 1983.

Computer Notes:

CHAPTER 1: LECTURE NOTES
INTRODUCTION AND MATHEMATICAL CONCEPTS

The Nature of Physics (p. 1)

Units (p. 2)
    Systems of Units

    Definition of Standard Units

    Base Units and Derived Units

The Role of Units in Problem Solving (p. 4)

    The Conversion of Units

    Units as a Problem Solving Aid

CHAPTER 1: LECTURE NOTES

Trigonometry (p. 6)

    Basic Trigonometric Functions

    The Pythagorean Theorem

The Nature of Physical Quantities: Scalars and Vectors (p. 8)

    Scalars

    Vectors

    Symbols Used for Scalars and Vectors

Vector Addition and Subtraction (p. 10)

    Addition of Colinear Vectors

    Addition of Perpendicular Vectors

CHAPTER 1: LECTURE NOTES

Addition of Vectors That Are Neither Colinear nor Perpendicular

Subtraction of Vectors

Vector Components (p. 12)

The Meaning of Vector Components

Resolving a Vector into Its Components

Vectors That Have Zero Components

Vectors That Are Equal

Addition of Vectors by Means of Vector Components (p. 14)

CHAPTER 1: NEXT TIME NOTES

CHAPTER 2: TEACHING AIDS

KINEMATICS IN ONE DIMENSION

Transparencies:

Figure 2.3: Velocity changes with time as a plane accelerates during take-off.

Figure 2.4: Velocity of the plane changes by +9 km/h during each second.

Figure 2.6: Velocity and acceleration are in opposite directions for this car.

Figure 2.14: The displacement **s** and the velocity **v** of a freely falling body are illustrated for the first five seconds after being dropped from rest.

Solved Problems:

Text Problem 21 is Study Guide Practice Problem 5.

Text Problem 49 is Study Guide Practice Problem 9.

Text Problem 43 is Study Guide Practice Problem 11.

Spreadsheet:

#03: Objects Falling Freely from Buildings

Demonstrations:

Freier and Anderson Mb-10, 13, 15, 18, 21, 22;

Hilton M-2 - 5;

Meiners 7-1.2

1. Acceleration due to gravity: Hold a notebook and a single sheet of paper side by side (in a horizontal plane) and drop them simultaneously. Students usually assert that the single sheet fell more slowly because a larger air resistance acted on it. In fact, the air resistance on the notebook was larger because it had a larger velocity. However, as a percentage of the object's weight, the air resistance on the single sheet was larger. To reduce the effect of air resistance, place the sheet on top of the notebook; be sure it doesn't extend beyond the edges. Then both objects will fall with the same acceleration. The same effect can be achieved by crumpling the single sheet into a small ball.

Films:

Video Vignette: Leaning Tower of Pisa

Straight-Line Kinematics (PSSC), 16mm, b/w, 34 min., MLA

Galileo's Laws of Falling Bodies, 16mm, b/w, 6 min., EBEC

Velocity and Acceleration, 16mm, b/w, 12 min., Coronet

Laboratory:

Bernard and Epp: #7: Uniformly Accelerated Motion

Preston: #2: Velocity and Acceleration

Computer Resources for Chapter 2

Programs:

1. *The Microcomputer Based Lab Project Motion* (HRM) is useful for helping students interpret kinematic graphs. As a student moves back and forth in front of a sonar ranging device, his position, velocity, or acceleration is potted on the monitor of an Apple II computer. Several sonic rangers are reviewed in TPT January 1988.

2. *Motion. Cross.* Apple II+. Generates graphs of coordinate, velocity, and acceleration for one dimensional motion. Has tutorial sections on one dimensional translational and rotational kinematics and dynamics. Reviewed TPT September 1983.

Projects:

1. Have students use the root finding ability of Eureka or their own computer programs to solve kinematic problems. Nearly every one of them can be set up as a problem that involves finding the square root of either the coordinate or velocity as a function of time, followed perhaps by substitution of the root in another kinematics equation. Can handle problems involving non-constant accelration such as, for example, when air resistance is included.

Computer Notes:

CHAPTER 2: LECTURE NOTES
KINEMATICS IN ONE DIMENSION

The Description of Motion (p. 22)

Displacement (p. 23)

Speed and Velocity (p. 24)

Average Speed

Average Velocity

Instantaneous Velocity

CHAPTER 2: LECTURE NOTES

Acceleration (p. 27)

Equations of Kinematics for Constant Acceleration (p. 30)

Applications of the Equations of Kinematics (p. 33)

CHAPTER 2: LECTURE NOTES

Freely Falling Bodies (p. 37)

Freely Falling Bodies and the Equations of Kinematics

Symmetry in the Motion of Freely Falling Bodies

Graphical Analysis of Velocity and Acceleration for Linear Motion (p. 40)

CHAPTER 2: NEXT TIME NOTES

CHAPTER 3: TEACHING AIDS

KINEMATICS IN TWO DIMENSIONS

Transparencies:

Figure 3.9: A package released from rest has the same vertical motion as one thrown horizontally from the same height.

Figure 3.12: A 40° trajectory has the same range as a 50° trajectory.

Solved Problems:

Text Problem 11 is Study Guide Example 3.

Text Problem 23 is Study Guide Practice Problem 4.

Spreadsheet:

#06: Understanding Data (Marbles Rolling Off Tables)

Demonstrations:

Freier and Anderson Mb-14, 16, 17, 19, 20, 23, 24, 28;

Hilton M-13;

Meiners 7-2.7, 7-2.11

1. Projectile Motion: Place a small iron sheet on a toy animal (traditionally a monkey) and attach to an electromagnet. Boresight a metal tube on the monkey, place a steel ball in the tube, and fire (by blowing or by using compressed air). A trip wire at end of tube opens the electromagnet as ball emerges from tube. A collision always occurs (if the bullet has sufficient range). An interesting variation is to announce that the monkey is still alive, whereupon an assistant rushes forth shooting a cap pistol.

Films:

Video Vignettes:　　The Ballet Dancer
　　　　　　　　　　Artificial Motions
　　　　　　　　　　Spin on a Tennis Ball
　　　　　　　　　　The Baseball Bat

Free Fall and Projectile Motion (PSSC), 16mm, b/w, 27 min., MLA

Vector Kinematics (PSSC), 16mm, b/w, 16 min., MLA

Accelerated Motion and Angle of Lean, 3/4" videocassette, color, 9 min., NTSU

Laboratory:

Bernard and Epp: #11:　　Inelastic Impact and the Velocity of a Projectile (Procedures A and B)

Preston: #3: Two-Dimensional Projectile Motion

Computer Resources for Chapter 3

Programs:

1. *Personal Problems*. Addison-Wesley. Apple II. The program plots the trajectories of projectiles subjected to air resistance. It also plots the coordinates, velocity components, and acceleration components as functions of time and lists values for points along the trajectory. The user can specify the initial conditions and the coefficient of air resistance. Use this as an alternative to student programming. Reviewed TPT December 1985.

2. *Physics Simulations I: Ballistics*. Kinko's. Macintosh. Plots trajectories of projectiles, with or without a drag force proportional to velocity. Drag coefficient can be constant or depend exponentially on altitude. Exellent for illustrating lectures.

3. *Motion*. See Chapter 2 notes.

4. *Newton's Laws*. J&S. Apple II. F = ma drill problems. Reviewed TPT February 1984.

5. *Mechanics*. Edutech. Apple IIe, II+. Demonstrates vertical fall with or without air resistance, hunter and monkey experiment, planetary motion.

Projects:

1. Have students use *Eureka* or their own root finding programs to solve projectile problems. It is instructive to have them plot the velocity components as functions of time for a projectile subject to air resistance. Consider initial velocities which are both greater and less than the terminal velocity. Also have them study the maximum height and range of projectiles with various coefficients of air resistance.

Computer Notes:

CHAPTER 3: LECTURE NOTES
KINEMATICS IN TWO DIMENSIONS

Displacement, Velocity and Acceleration (p. 50)

Displacement

Velocity

Acceleration

Equations of Kinematics in Two Dimensions (p. 51)

CHAPTER 3: LECTURE NOTES

Projectile Motion (p. 54)

CHAPTER 3: LECTURE NOTES

Relative Velocity (p. 59)

Relative Velocity in One Dimension

Relative Velocity in Two Dimensions

CHAPTER 3: NEXT TIME NOTES

CHAPTER 4: TEACHING AIDS
FORCES AND NEWTON'S LAWS OF MOTION

Transparencies:
Figure 4.4: The role of inertia in the operation of a seat belt.
Figure 4.10: The gravitational force between two uniform spheres of matter.
Figure 4.17: Force of static friction.

Solved Problems:
Text Problem 35 is Study Guide Practice Problem 6.
Text Problem 17 is Study Guide Practice Problem 9.

Spreadsheets: None

Demonstrations:
Inertia: Freier and Anderson Mc-1 - 5;
                Hilton M-6;
                Meiners 8-2.2, 8-2.3, 8-2.4
Second Law: Freier and Anderson Md-2;
                Hilton M-7;
                Meiners 8-1.8
Third Law: Freier and Anderson Md-1, 3, 4;
                Hilton M-8;
                Meiners 8-4.3, 8-4.7

1. Inertia: An air track is an excellent way to demonstrate inertia. We are so accustomed to seeing objects slow down due to friction that we are amazed when a glider on the air track moves from one end to the other after receiving only a slight push. Most campuses have a game room with an air hockey table; this is the two-dimensional counterpart of the air track.

2. Second Law: The air track can also be used to demonstrate Newton's second law. Attach a string to a glider, pass the string over a pulley at the end of the track, and suspend varying weights from the string to show that acceleration is proportional to force. Then keep the suspended weight constant and place varying masses on the glider. Actually, the tension in the string that pulls the glider is smaller than the suspended weight.

Films:
Video Vignette: Leaning Tower of Pisa
A Million to One (PSSC), 16mm, b/w, 5 min., MLA
Action and Reaction, 16mm color, 14 min., FA
The Laws of Sliding Friction, 16mm, b/w, 6 min., Purdue
Principles of Lubrication, 16mm, color, 23 min., IFB

60

Laboratory:

Preston: #4: Newton's Second Law

Computer Resources for Chapter 4

Programs:

1. *Physics: Elementary Mechanics*. Control Data. Apple II, IBM PC. Drill problems in collisions, gravitation, satellite motion, rotational dynamics, harmonic motion. Statements of problems are not complete and students must ask the computer for additional data. Helps students think about what information is required to solve mechanical problems. Reviewed TPT May 1986.

Computer Notes:

CHAPTER 4: LECTURE NOTES
FORCES AND NEWTON'S LAWS OF MOTION

The Concepts of Force and Mass (p. 70)

Newton's First Law of Motion (p. 71)

Inertia and Mass

An Inertial Reference Frame

Newton's Second Law of Motion (p. 73)

Units and the Second Law

Free-Body Diagrams and the Second Law

CHAPTER 4: LECTURE NOTES

Newton's First Law as a Special Case of the Second Law

The Vector Nature of Newton's Second Law of Motion (p. 76)

Newton's Third Law of Motion (p. 77)

The Gravitational Force (p. 78)

Newton's Law of Universal Gravitation

Measurement of the Universal Gravitational Constant

The Weight of an Object

Relation Between Mass and Weight

CHAPTER 4: LECTURE NOTES

The Normal Force (p. 83)

Frictional Forces (p. 85)

Static Frictional Force

Kinetic Frictional Force

The Tension Force (p. 89)

CHAPTER 4: NEXT TIME NOTES

CHAPTER 5: TEACHING AIDS

APPLICATIONS OF NEWTON'S LAWS OF MOTION

Transparencies:
Figure 5.4: A plane moving at constant velocity due to the action of four forces.
Figure 5.10: The apparent weight depends on the acceleration of the elevator.

Solved Problems:
Text Problem 37 is Study Guide Practice Problem 2
Text Problem 33 is Study Guide Practice Problem 5.

Spreadsheets:
#04: The Tower of Pisa Experiment
#05: Falling Parachutists
#12: Launching a Rocket
#19: Pulling a Car Out of the Mud

Demonstrations:
Freier and Anderson Mf-1, 2, Mj-2, Mk-4;
Hilton M-3a, d, M-7c;
Meiners 7-1.6, 8-1.4, 8-2.5

Films:
Inertia (PSSC). 16mm, b/w, 26 min., MLA
A Million to One (PSSC), 16mm, b/w, 4 min., MLA
Can you figure out the rationale for the film's title? Show this film if at all possible. It shows a massive (about 3 kg) dry ice puck being pulled across a nearly frictionless horizontal surface by a trained flea (whose usual employment is in a circus sideshow act). This performance, filmed in 1959, is narrated by its creator, Edward M. Purcell, winner of the Nobel Prize for Physics in 1952 and now (1988) Emeritus Professor of Physics at Harvard. I always tell this to students; they're amazed and amused to learn that physicists really aren't so stuffy. Then I tell them that this originally was part a longer film (the one listed above) that Purcell created and narrated. There is an interesting story surrounding removal of the flea episode from the original film and its release some years later as a separate film. I'll not relate the story here, but if you're interested in knowing, drop me a line and I'll share it with you. I do tell the story to my classes.

Laboratory:
Bernard and Epp: #4:   Composition and Resolution of Forces--
Force Table Method

Computer Resources for Chapter 5

Programs:

1. *Mechanics*. See notes for Chapter 3.

2. *Physics: Elementary Mechanics.* See notes for Chapter 4.

Computer Notes:

CHAPTER 5: LECTURE NOTES
APPLICATIONS OF NEWTON'S LAWS OF MOTION

The Significance of Newton's Laws of Motion (p. 94)

Equilibrium Applications of Newton's Laws of Motion (p. 95)

Definition of Equilibrium

Steps in Solving Equilibrium Problems

Examples of Equilibrium Problems

CHAPTER 5: LECTURE NOTES

Non-Equilibrium Applications of Newton's Laws of Motion (p. 100)

Steps in Solving Non-Equilibrium Problems

Examples of Non-Equilibrium Problems

CHAPTER 5: LECTURE NOTES

Apparent Weight (p. 104)

CHAPTER 5: NEXT TIME NOTES

CHAPTER 6: TEACHING AIDS
DYNAMICS OF UNIFORM CIRCULAR MOTION

Transparencies:
Figure 6.11: A synchronous satellite orbits the earth in a circular orbit that is in the plane of the equator.

Figure 6.12: Weightlessness: A person in an elevator during free-fall and an astronaut in orbit around the earth.

Figure 6.13: The surface of a rotating space station pushes on objects in contact with it and thereby provides the centripetal force needed to keep them moving on a circular orbit.

Solved Problems:
Text Problem 13 is Study Guide Example 4.

Spreadsheets:
#07: Ferris Wheel Rides
#13: Inserting a Rocket into Orbit

Demonstrations:
Freier and Anderson Mf-1, 2, Mj-2, Mk-4;
Hilton M-3a, d, M-7c, M-16b, f;
Meiners 7-1.6, 8-1.4, 8-2.5

Films:
Video Vignettes: The Ferris Wheel
                   The Roller Coaster
Inertial Forces, Translational Acceleration, S8, color, 3 min., Kalmia
Inertial Forces, Centripetal Acceleration, S8, color, 3 min., Kalmia
Frames of Reference (PSSC), 16mm b/w, 28 min., MLA

This is THE classic film among physics instruction films; it's the MONA LISA. Made in 1959 by two Canadian physicists (University of Toronto), it immediately became a hit and remains so to this day. If you have time for only one film, this is the one. In fact, if you have time for no films at all, show this anyway. I routinely show about two-thirds of this movie to my theoretical mechanics class (seniors and beginning graduate students). Yes, they do snicker upon noticing that the film byline indicates that it was made for a high school physics course but at least they make an effort to conceal their smirks. Some of my esteemed colleagues do the former but, alas, not the latter. You look at the movie and judge whether it's worth fifteen minutes of class time in theoretical mechanics. I'd be interested in hearing your opinion.

Laboratory:
Bernard and Epp: 13: Centripetal Force

Computer Resources for Chapter 6

Programs:

1. *Mechanics*. See notes for Chapter 3.
2. *Physics Simulations I: Kepler*. Kinko's. Macintosh. Plots orbits of one or two planets, with parameters set by user. Use to illustrate lectures or ask students to look at some interesting orbits.
3. *Physics: Elementary Mechanics*. See notes for Chapter 4.

Computer Notes:

CHAPTER 6: LECTURE NOTES
DYNAMICS OF UNIFORM CIRCULAR MOTION

Uniform Circular Motion (p. 114)

Centripetal Acceleration (p. 114)

Centripetal Force (p. 117)

CHAPTER 6: LECTURE NOTES

Banked Curves (p. 119)

Satellites in Circular Orbits (p. 120)

The Relation Between Orbital Radius and Orbital Speed

The Period of the Satellite

CHAPTER 6: LECTURE NOTES

Apparent Weightlessness and Artifical Gravity (p. 122)

Vertical Circular Motion (p. 123)

CHAPTER 6: NEXT TIME NOTES

CHAPTER 7: TEACHING AIDS

WORK AND ENERGY

Transparencies:

Figure 7.3: The bench press: Weight lifter raises and lowers a weight.
Figure 7.6: The engine of this space probe is doing positive work.
Figure 7.12: A bobsled illustrates conservation of total mechanical energy.

Solved Problems:

Text Problem 5 is Study Guide Example 3.
Text Problem 23 is Study Guide Example 7.
Text Problem 37 is Study Guide Example 9.

Spreadsheets:

#09: A Jet Airplane Landing
#10: The Stopping Distance of Cars

Demonstrations:

Work: Freier and Anderson Mv-1
Power: Freier and Anderson Mv-2
Conservation of Energy: Freier and Anderson Mn-1 - 3, 6;
                            Hilton M-14a, b, e;
                            Meiners 9-1.3

1. Push the Wall: In my class I go over to the wall and push on it. Everyone agrees that the wall did not move (after all, I'm not Samson); they also agree that you can get very tired if you push on the wall for a while. But if there's no displacement of the wall, there is no work. Sometimes I'll leave this paradox with them until the next class, at which time I take a bow and arrow and prepare to shoot. With a little coaxing, they concede that I'm quivering slightly and so the bow is moving--so was the wall, etc.

Films:

Conservation of Energy (PSSC), 16mm, b/w, 27 min., MLA
Energy and Work (PSSC), 16mm, b/w, 28 min., MLA
Perpetual Motion, 16mm, color, 11 min., BFA
Gravitational Potential Energy; Kinetic Energy; Conservation of Energy:
    Pole Vault; S8, color, 3 min. each, Kalmia

Laboratory:

Bernard and Epp: #9: Work, Energy, and Friction
                  #10: Mechanical Advantage and Efficiency of Simple Machines
Preston: #6: Conservation of Mechanical Energy

Computer Resources for Chapter 7

Programs:

1. *Work and Energy*. J&S. Apple II. Drill problems on computation of work, work-energy theorem, and conservation of energy.

2. *Physics 1: Module F. Work, Kinetic Energy, and Power*. Control Data. Apple II or IBM PC. Tutorial.

3. *Work, Energy, and Power*. Merlan. Apple II. Tutorial.

4. *Personal Problems*. Addison-Wesley. Apple II. Program on inverse square orbits; plots open and closed orbits, given initial conditions. Numerical values of energy and angular momentum can be obtained for any point on orbit. An impulse can be applied to the object at any point in its motion. Excellent for lecture demonstrations.

Computer Notes:

CHAPTER 7: LECTURE NOTES
WORK AND ENERGY

Work (p. 131)

Work Done by a Force That Points in the Direction of The Motion

Work Done by A Force that Points at an Angle to the Direction of Motion

Positive and Negative Work

The Work-Energy Theorem and Kinetic Energy (p. 135)

CHAPTER 7: LECTURE NOTES

Gravitational Potential Energy (p. 138)

Work Done by the Force of Gravity

Gravitational Potential Energy

The Conservation of Mechanical Energy (p. 141)

CHAPTER 7: LECTURE NOTES

Conservative Forces and Mechanical Energy (p. 144)

Power (p. 145)

Other Forms of Energy and the Conservation of Energy (p. 147)

CHAPTER 7: NEXT TIME NOTES

CHAPTER 8: TEACHING AIDS

IMPULSE AND MOMENTUM

Transparencies:
Figure 8.1:   A bat exerts a force on a baseball, thereby changing its momentum.
Figure 8.6:   Elastic and inelastic collisions.
Figure 8.9:   A rocket gains momentum as hot gases are ejected.

Solved Problems: None

Spreadsheets:
#14: Small Cars Colliding
#15: A Bouncing Golf Ball

Demonstrations:
Freier and Anderson Mg-4, 5, Mh-1 - 5, Mi-2;
Hilton M-15;
Meiners 9-4.19

1.   The Egg Hits the Sheet: Have two students with long arms grasp the corners of a bed sheet, hold it vertically, and then move the lower hands slightly forward and upward. This forms a pocket at the bottom and also assures that the sheet is not taut. Have a student stand a few feet in front of the sheet and throw a raw egg (that has no cracks, even hairline ones) so as to hit the sheet near the middle. Even if the egg is hurled by a major league pitcher, it is most unlikely to break. In presenting this demonstration I once asked an attractive but rather ungainly blonde to do the hurling. She completely missed the sheet; talk about a mess--yuck!

Films:
Video Vignette: The Baseball Bat
Collision of Hard Spheres (PSSC), 16mm b/w, 19 min., MLA
Tailgating: How Close Is Too Close?, 16mm color, 11 min., AIMS
Human Momenta (NASA Skylab), S8, color, 3 min., AAPT
Two Dimensional Collisions I and II, S8, color, 3 min. each, Kalmia

Laboratory:
Bernard and Epp: #8: Impulse and Momentum
                            #12: Elastic Collision--Momentum and Energy
                                       Relations in Two Dimensions
Preston: #7: Conservation of Kinetic Energy and Momentum in
                     Collisions

Computer Resources for Chapter 8

Programs:

1. *Collisions on an Air Track*. Cambridge. Apple II. Chiefly tutorial but includes segments suitable for lecture illustrations. User specified collisions are simulated and in each case a numerical analysis of dynamic quantities (velocity, momentum, kinetic energy) is given. Reviewed TPT September 1985.

Projects:

1. Have students use *Eureka* or write a program to graph the total final kinetic energy as a function of the final velocity of one object in a two body , one dimensional collision, given the initial velocities and masses of the two objects. Ask them to run the program for specific initial conditions and indentify elastic, completely inelastic, and explosive collisions on their graphs.

Interactive Videodisk:

1. *Physics and Automobile Collisions* by Dean Zollman. The disk shows collisions of cars with fixed barriers and two car collisions (head-on, at 90o, and at 60o). One sequence shows the influence of bumper design, others show the influence of air bags and shoulder straps on mannikins. All are slow motion films of manufacturers' tests and many show grids and clocks. Students can stop the action to take measurements, then make calculations of momentum and energy transfers. For most exercises a commercial player is satisfactory; for a few a computer controlled player is required.

Computer Notes:

CHAPTER 8: LECTURE NOTES
IMPULSE AND MOMENTUM

Introduction (p. 156)

The Impulse-Momentum Theorem (p. 157)

Definition of Impulse

Definition of Linear Momentum

Impulse-Momentum Theorem

The Principle of Conservation of Linear Momentum (p. 159)

CHAPTER 8: LECTURE NOTES

CHAPTER 8: LECTURE NOTES

Rocket Propulsion (p. 167)

CHAPTER 8: NEXT TIME NOTES

CHAPTER 9: TEACHING AIDS
ROTATIONAL KINEMATICS

Transparencies:

Figure 9.1: An object undergoing rotation without translation.

Figure 9.10: A model airplane undergoing uniform circular motion.

Figure 9.11: (a) As an automobile moves with a linear speed, it's wheels roll along the ground and have an angular speed with respect to the axles.

(b) If the wheels roll without slipping, the distance through which an axle moves is equal to the circular arc length traveled by a point on the outer edge of the tire.

Figure 9.12: The angular velocity is directed along the axis of rotation.

Figure 9.13: The angular acceleration is directed along the axis of rotation.

Solved Problems:

Text Problem 7 is Study Guide Practice Problem 1

Spreadsheet:

#16: The Rotational Speed of Compact Discs

Demonstrations:

Freier and Anderson Mb-4, 10, 30, Mr-4;
Hilton M-16a;
Meiners 12-2.1

1. A Lifetime Going Around in Circles: Ask the class: "Do you know people who just go around in circles?" Then remind them that all of us on Planet Earth are going around on (or along) a circle. (Ignore the earth going around the sun for now.) How many rev/day? How many rad/day? How many rad/sec?.

2. Linear and Angular Speeds: See #1 above. Ask how fast is a point on the earth's equator moving. Sadly, almost no one will know. How far is it around the earth at the equator? And how much time does it take to go all the way around? So we get approximately 1000 mi/h. They'll be amazed.

Films:

Video Vignettes: The Roller Coaster
The Baseball Bat

Laboratory: None suggested

Computer Resources for Chapter 9

Programs:

1. *Motion.* See notes for Chapter 2.

Projects:

1. Ask students to use *Eureka* or their own root finding programs to solve rotational kinematic problems.

Computer Notes:

CHAPTER 9: LECTURE NOTES
ROTATIONAL KINEMATICS

Rotational Motion and Angular Displacement (p. 173)

Angular Velocity and Angular Acceleration (p. 176)

Angular Velocity

Angular Acceleration

CHAPTER 9: LECTURE NOTES

The Equations of Rotational Kinematics (p. 178)

Angular Variables and Tangential Variables (p. 180)

Centripetal Acceleration and Tangential Acceleration (p. 180)

CHAPTER 9: LECTURE NOTES

Rolling Motion (p. 182)

The Vector Nature of Angular Variables (p. 183)

CHAPTER 9: NEXT TIME NOTES

CHAPTER 10: TEACHING AIDS
ROTATIONAL DYNAMICS

Transparencies:
Figure 10.2: The torque produced by a given force depends on the lever arm.
Figure 10.4: (a) Translational motion.
(b) Combined translational and rotational motion.
Figure 10.10: The center of gravity of two objects: A board with a box on it.

Solved Problems:
Text Problem 37 is Study Guide Practice Problem 8.

Spreadsheets:
#11: Center of Mass
#17: Diving from a High Board
#18: Forces in Limbs

Demonstrations:
Torque: Freier and Anderson Mo-5;
            Meiners 12-4.9
Free Fall Paradox: Hilton M-19k
Rotational Dynamics: Freier and Anderson Fs-7, Mo-3, Ms-6, 7, Mt-5, 6;
            Hilton M-10d;
            Meiners 12-4.3, 12-5.2
Angular Momentum: Freier and Anderson Mt-1 - 4, 6, 7, Mu-1;
            Hilton M-8b, M-19i;
            Meiners 12-3.1
Gyroscope: Freier and Anderson Mu-2 - 18;
            Hilton M-19a, b, f, g, h
Conservation of Energy: Freier and Anderson Mr-1, 5, Ms-1, 2, 3;
            Hilton M-19c
Moment of Inertia: Freier and Anderson Ms-4;
            Meiners 12-3.3

Films:
Video Vignettes: The Ferris Wheel;   Artificial Motions
            The Ballet Dancer;   The Baseball Bat
Angular Momentum: A Vector Quantity (PSSC), 16mm, b/w, 27 min., MLA
Gyroscopes in Space, 16mm color, 14 min., NASA
Conservation Laws in Zero-G, 16mm color, 18 min., NASA
Games Astronauts Play; Acrobatic Astronauts, S8, color, 4 min. each, NASA

Laboratory:

Bernard and Epp: #5: Balanced Torques and Center of Gravity
#6: Equilibrium of a Crane;
#14: Moment of Inertia

Preston: #8: Bicycles, Boomerang, and Gyroscope

Computer Resources for Chapter 10

Programs:

1. *Statics*. *Cross*. Apple II+. Tutorial on solving equilibrium problems, examples, problems for students to solve. Reviewed TPT February 1983.

Computer Notes:

CHAPTER 10: LECTURE NOTES
ROTATIONAL DYNAMICS

Torque (p. 192)

Rigid Objects in Equilibrium (p. 194)

Translational and Rotational Motion

Equilibrium

The Axis Used for Calculating the Torque Is Arbitrary

CHAPTER 10: LECTURE NOTES

Determination of the Lever Arms

Selecting the Directions of the Forces in the Free-Body Diagram

Center of Gravity (p. 199)

Newton's Second Law for Rotational Motion (p. 202)

CHAPTER 10: LECTURE NOTES

Rotational Work and Energy (p. 207)

Rotational Work

Rotational Kinetic Energy

Angular Momentum (p. 210)

Definition of Angular Momentum

Principle of Conservation of Angular Momentum

CHAPTER 10: NEXT TIME NOTES

CHAPTER 11: TEACHING AIDS

ELASTICITY AND SIMPLE HARMONIC MOTION

Transparencies:
Figure 11.12: Position as a function of time for a simple harmonic oscillator.
Figure 11.14: Simple harmonic motion is executed by the shadow of an object undergoing uniform circular motion.

Solved Problems:
None

Spreadsheets:
#21: The Size of Grandfather Clocks
#22: Damped Oscillations

Demonstrations:
Elasticity: Freier and Anderson Ma-8, 9, 10, 12, 13, Mw-3;
               Hilton M-19j
Simple Harmonic Motion: Meiners 15-1.1, 15-1.2, 15-1.3, 15-1.8, 15-1.9
Spring: Freier and Anderson Mx-1 - 4, 7;
           Hilton M-14e
Pendula: Freier and Anderson Mx-6, 9 - 12, My-1 - 3, 8; Mz-1, 2, 3, 6, 7, 9;
            Hilton M-14d, f

1. Graphing SHM: Attach a very small flashlight to the end of a spring loaded to give a SHM period of a few seconds. Turn off the class lights, turn on the flashlight, set load into vibration, and walk across the room to get a graph of displacement versus time.

2. Untitled: Attach an harmonica to a spring and vibrate (or to a string and swing). Ask: What's this? **SIMPLE HARMONICA MOTION.** NOTE: I picked this demonstration up in April 1988 from Dr. D. Rae Carpenter, Jr. and Dr. Richard B. Minnix from Virginia Military Institute. They are outstanding physics demonstrators. See them if at all possible.

Films:
Video Vignette: The Grandfather Clock
Simple Harmonic Motion, 16mm, color, 17 min, PSU
Periodic Motions (PSSC), 16mm, b/w, 33 min., MLA
Coupled Oscillators: (1) Equal Masses, (2) Unequal Masses; The Wilberforce Pendulum; Tacoma Narrows Bridge Collapse, S8, color, 3 min. each, Kalmia

Laboratory:
Bernard and Epp: #15: Elasticity and Vibratory Motion
Preston: #9: Periodic Motion

Computer Resources for Chapter 11

Programs:

1. *Harmonic Motion Workshop*. High. Apple II, II+, IIe. Simulation of simple harmonic motion. Displays velocity vector, acceleration vector, kinetic energy, potential energy. Damped and undamped. Useful for lectures. Reviewed TPT October 1983.

2. *Physics Simulations I: Oscillator*. Kinko's. Macintosh. Displays a mass in simple harmonic motion, damped or undamped. Plots position, potential energy, and kinetic energy as functions of time.

Computer Notes:

CHAPTER 11: LECTURE NOTES
ELASTICITY AND SIMPLE HARMONIC MOTION

Introduction (p. 224)

Elastic Deformation (p. 225)

    Stretching, Compression, and Young's Modulus

    Shear Deformation and the Shear Modulus

    Volume Deformation and the Bulk Modulus

Stress, Strain and Hooke's Law (p. 228)

CHAPTER 11: LECTURE NOTES

The Ideal Spring and Simple Harmonic Motion (p. 230)

Simple Harmonic Motion and the Reference Circle (p. 233)

Displacement

Velocity

Acceleration

Frequency of Vibration

CHAPTER 11: LECTURE NOTES

Energy and Simple Harmonic Motion (p. 238)

Elastic Potential Energy

The Conservation of Mechanical Energy

The Pendulum (p. 241)

Damped Harmonic Motion (p. 243)

Driven Harmonic Motion and Resonance (p. 243)

CHAPTER 11: NEXT TIME NOTES

CHAPTER 12: TEACHING AIDS

FLUID STATICS

Transparencies:
Figure 12.5: Vertical forces acting on a column of fluid.
Figure 12.16: When an object is floating, the buoyant force equals the weight.

Solved Problems:
None

Spreadsheets:
#25: Hydraulic Brakes of a Car
#26: Magdeburg Hemispheres

Demonstrations:

Liquid Pressure: Freier and Anderson Fa, Fb, Fc;
Hilton M-20b

Air Pressure: Freier and Anderson Fd;
Hilton M-22d;
Meiners 16-4.5, 16-4.6

Siphons: Freier and Anderson Fe;
Meiners 16-4.11

Pressure Gauges: Freier and Anderson Ff;
Hilton M-22b

Density: Freier and Anderson Fh;
Hilton M-20a, M-22a; M-22e

Archimedes' Principle: Freier and Anderson Fg;
Hilton M-20c, M-22c;
Meiners 16-2.5, 16-2.6

Pascal's Principle: Hilton M-20e;
Meiners 16-2.2

1. Buoyancy and Newton's Third Law: Fill a flask to a level of about 10 cm. Place the flask and a metal cylinder of height < 10 cm side by side on the pan of a scale; balance scale. (a) Ask: If cylinder is now put into flask and touches the bottom, will the scale still be in balance? Do it so class can see that balance is preserved. Why? Most students think it's because there's no water between the cylinder and bottom of beaker. (b) Tie a string around the neck of the flask; attach cylinder to other end of string. Ask: If cylinder is now placed into flask such that the cylinder is completely submerged and not touching the sides or bottom, will scale still be balanced? Try it and help class to rediscover Newton's Third Law.

Films:

Fluids in Weightlessness, 16mm, color, 14 min., NASA

Specific Gravity and Archimedes' Principle, 16mm, color, 11 min., Coronet

Laboratory:

Bernard and Epp: #16: Buoyancy of Liquids and Specific Gravity

Computer Resources for Chapters 12

Programs:

1. *Phys. Software Lib. Disk 15: Continuum Mechanics--Fluid Statics*. Allyn and Bacon. Apple II. Tutorial on fluid pressure, Archimedes' Principle, Pascal's Principle, etc.

Computer Notes:

CHAPTER 12: LECTURE NOTES
FLUID STATICS

The Nature of Fluids (p. 252)

Mass Density (p. 253)

Pressure (p. 254)

CHAPTER 12: LECTURE NOTES

The Relation Between Pressure and Depth in a Static Fluid (p. 256)

Pressure Gauges (p. 259)

CHAPTER 12: LECTURE NOTES

Pascal's Principle (p. 261)

Archimedes' Principle (p. 262)

CHAPTER 12: NEXT TIME NOTES

CHAPTER 13: TEACHING AIDS

FLUID DYNAMICS

Transparencies:
Figure 13.14: Streamlines of air flow around an airplane wing, an airplane, and a race car.

Figure 13.15: Bernouilli's effect causes a spinning baseball to curve.

Solved Problems:
Text Problem 3 is Study Guide Example 2.

Text Problem 7 is Study Guide Example 4.

Text Problem 23 is Study Guide Practice Problem 7.

Spreadsheets:
#27: Leaky Water Cylinder

#28: Heart Attack Risks

Demonstrations:
Freier and Anderson Fj-1 - 11, Fk-2, Fl-1;

Meiners 17-2.5, 17-2.12

1. Air Foil (Bernoulli): Grasp a sheet of paper (letter size or so) by the two corners along a narrow side. Hold this side just below the mouth and blow across the drooping side. The droopy side will rise.

2. Bernoulli: Attach the stem of a funnel to a compressed air source. Hold the funnel vertically upward and place a ping-pong ball into the funnel. Ask: How high do you think ball will go when I turn on compressed air? As you prepare to turn on compressed air, look upward and note that you are directly beneath a fluorescent light. Move off to the side just to be safe. Turn on the air. Do your best to look surprised that the ball is pulled downward rather than being pushed upward.

Films:
Video Vignettes: Leaning Tower of Pisa

Spin on a Tennis Ball

Bernoulli's Principle, 16mm, b/w, 30 min., EBEC

Mechanics of Fluids: Introduction to the Study of Fluid Motion, 16mm, color 25 min., UIAVC

Laboratory:
Preston: #13: Motion of Fluids

Computer Resources for Chapter 13

Programs:

1. *Phys. Software Lib. Disk 16: Continuum Mechanics--Fluid Dynamics.* Allyn and Bacon. Apple II. Tutorial on fluids in motion.

Computer Notes:

CHAPTER 13: LECTURE NOTES
FLUID DYNAMICS

Fluids in Motion and Streamlines (p. 273)

Steady or Unsteady Flow

Compressible or Incompressible Flow

Viscous or Nonviscous Flow

Rotational or Irrotational Flow

The Equation of Continuity (p. 276)

CHAPTER 13: LECTURE NOTES

Bernoulli's Equation (p. 278)

Applications of Bernoulli's Equation (p. 281)

CHAPTER 13: LECTURE NOTES

Viscous Flow (p. 285)

Viscosity

Poiseuille's Law

CHAPTER 13: NEXT TIME NOTES

CHAPTER 14: TEACHING AIDS
TEMPERATURE AND THERMAL EXPANSION

Transparencies:
Figure 14.1: The Celsius and Fahrenheit temperature scales.
Figure 14.3: A constant-volume gas thermometer.
Figure 14.12: A bimetallic strip used for controlling the brewing time on an automatic coffee maker.

Solved Problems: None.

Spreadsheets: None.

Demonstrations:

Thermometers:	Freier and Anderson Ha-1 - 4;
	Hilton H-1; Meiners 25-2.3
Thermal Expansion:	Freier and Anderson Ha-5 - 12, Hm-4;
	Hilton H-2;
	Meiners 25-2.1, 25-2.2
Thermal Properties:	Freier and Anderson Hk-7,9,10

1. Thermal Expansion. Several simple demonstration devices are available from science supply companies (Fisher, CENCO, etc). Almost all stock the **ball and ring device**. A brass sphere will barely pass through a brass ring at room temperature. Most of my students guess that if the ring is heated, the hole will be smaller and thus the sphere will not pass through--but it does. If the sphere is now heated (the ring having cooled in the meanwhile), the sphere will not pass through. If both ring and sphere are heated, the sphere will still fit through. If the ring is cooled with dry ice or liquid nitrogen, the sphere will not pass through.

Films:
Temperature and Matter, 16mm, color, 15 min., MCGH

Laboratory:
Bernard and Epp: #18: Linear Coefficient of Expansion in Metals
Preston: #10: Temperature

Computer Resources for Chapter 14

Programs:

1. *Phys. Software Lib. Disk 19: Macro-Properties of Thermal Systems*. Allyn and Bacon. Apple II. Tutorial.

Computer Notes:

CHAPTER 14: LECTURE NOTES
TEMPERATURE AND THERMAL EXPANSION

Tempertature and the Common Temperature Scales (p. 293)

The Celsius Scale

The Fahrenheit Scale

The Kelvin Temperature Scale (p. 295)

The Kelvin Scale

The Constant-Volume Gas Thermometer

Absolute Zero

122

CHAPTER 14: LECTURE NOTES

Thermometers (p. 297)

Thermometric Property

Thermocouple

Electrical Resistance Thermometers

Thermograph

Linear Thermal Expansion (p. 298)

Normal Solids

Thermal Stress

CHAPTER 14: LECTURE NOTES

The Bimetallic Strip

The Expansion of Holes

Volume Thermal Expansion (p. 303)

Normal Materials

The Anomalous Behavior of Water Near 4° C

CHAPTER 14: NEXT TIME NOTES

CHAPTER 15: TEACHING AIDS
HEAT ENERGY AND PHASE CHANGES

Transparencies:
Figure 15.3: Phase changes between solids, liquids, and gases.
Figure 15.10: Increasing the pressure on a gas at a temperature below and above the critical point.
Figure 15.14: Water vapor condenses as air flows past the cold coils of a dehumidifier.

Solved Problems:
Text Problem 15 is Study Guide Practice Problem 5.

Spreadsheets:
#29: Coffee Cooling in a Cup
#32: Mixing Hot and Cold Liquids

Demonstrations:
Specific Heat: Freier and Anderson Hb-1, 2
Change of Phase: Freier and Anderson Hj-1, 4, 7, 8, Hk-1, 3, 11;
Hilton M-5d, e;
Meiners 27-3.1, 27-3.6

1. Liquefied Gases: Very few of the students entering my college physics course have seen liquefied gases. Thus they are very impressed if a small dewar of liquid nitrogen is brought to class and some simple demonstrations performed. Something as simple as pouring some liquid nitrogen onto the lecture desk. Similarly, putting some chunks of dry ice in a beaker of water will get students' interest. Using two or three beakers with different colors of food dye in the water produces a nice effect.

Films:
Video Vignettes: Sunsets
Dropping Ice Cubes into Liquids
Heat Capacity and Changes of State, 16mm b/w, 30 min., EBEC
Critical Temperature, S8, color, 3 min., Kalmia

Laboratory:
Bernard and Epp: #19: Specific Heat and Temperature of a Hot Body
#20: Change of Phase -- Heat of Fusion and Heat of Vaporization
#21: Relative Humidity

Computer Resources for Chapter 15

Programs:

1. *Physics Vol. 6: Thermodynamics*. Cross. Apple II. Tutorial programs on calorimetry, p-V, p-T, and V-T diagrams, thermodynamic cycles, heat engines, and molecular motion. Reviewed TPT April 1985.
2. *Heats of Fusion/Vaporization*. Microphys. Apple II. Tutorial.

Computer Notes:

CHAPTER 15: LECTURE NOTES
HEAT ENERGY AND PHASE CHANGES

Internal Energy and Heat (p. 309)

Specific Heat Capacity (p. 311)

Solids and Liquids

Heat Units Other than the Joule

Gases

Calorimetry

CHAPTER 15: LECTURE NOTES

The Latent Heat of Phase Change (p. 315)

Phase Changes

Latent Heat of Fusion

Latent Heat of Vaporization

Latent Heat of Sublimation

The Phase Diagram (p. 318)

The Equilibrium Lines

CHAPTER 15: LECTURE NOTES

The Regions Between the Equilibrium Lines

The Triple Point

The Critical Point

Equilibrium Versus Nonequilibrium

Humidity (p. 323)

Absolute Humidity

Relative Humidity

CHAPTER 15: NEXT TIME NOTES

CHAPTER 16: TEACHING AIDS

THE TRANSFER OF HEAT ENERGY

Transparencies:
Figure 16.2: Convection currents for baseboard heater and refrigerator coils.
Figure 16.11:
Absorption and emission of radiation by a block coated with lamp-black and a block coated with silver.
Figure 16.13: Transfer of energy by convection, conduction, and radiation in a hot water solar collector.

Solved Problems: None

Spreadsheets:
#30: The Surface Temperature of the Moon
#31: Hot Rods

Demonstrations:
Convection: Freier and Anderson Hc-1, 2;
Hilton H-3a;
Meiners 26-3.6
Conduction:
Freier and Anderson Hd-1 - 7;
Hilton H-3a;
Meiners 26-3.1, 26-3.2, 26-3.4, 26-3.8
Radiation: Freier and Anderson Hf-1 - 5;
Hilton H-3b,c;
Meiners 38-5.1, 38-5.3, 38-5.4

1. Infrared Radiation: Students respond nicely to the detection of infrared radiation by a thermopile (and its galvanometer) placed near a person's forehead. I ask for three volunteers: a blonde, a redhead, and a brunette. I usually discuss thermography in medicine at this point. Also the determination of heat loss from a building by taking infrared pictures can be mentioned.

2. Radiometer: This is another inexpensive device that demonstrates the reflection and absorption of electromagnetic radiation to produce a difference in temperature between the white and black sides of the vanes.

Films:
Video Vignette: Sunsets

Laboratory:
Preston: #11: Heat Transfer

Computer Resources for Chapter 16

Programs:

1. *Thermodynamics I. Microphys*. Apple II. Tutorial.

Computer Notes:

CHAPTER 16: LECTURE NOTES
THE TRANSFER OF HEAT ENERGY

Introduction (p. 329)

Convection (p. 330)

Conduction (p. 333)

CHAPTER 16: LECTURE NOTES

Radiation (p. 337)

Electromagnetic Waves

Emission and Absorption

The Stefan-Boltzmann Law of Radiation

CHAPTER 16: LECTURE NOTES

Applications (p. 341)

CHAPTER 16: NEXT TIME NOTES

CHAPTER 17: TEACHING AIDS
THE IDEAL GAS LAW AND KINETIC THEORY

Transparencies:
Figure 17.7: Maxwell distribution curves for particle speeds in oxygen gas at temperatures of 300 and 1200 K.

Figure 17.12: A cross-sectional view of a leaf to indicate diffusion of water vapor through the stomatal pores.

Solved Problems:
Text Problem 29 is Study Guide Example 6.

Text Problem 41 is Study Guide Practice Problem 8.

Text Problem 25 is Study Guide Practice Problem 9.

Spreadsheet:
#33: Tire Pressures on a Long Trip

Demonstrations:
Kinetic Models: Freier and Anderson Hh-1, 2, 4, 5;
               Meiners 27-7.1, 27-7.5

Gas Laws: Freier and Anderson Hg-1,2,4;
         Hilton H-5f;
         Meiners 27-2.1, 27-2.7, 27-2.8

Brownian Motion: Freier and Anderson Hh-3;
               Meiners 27-7.6

Films:
Mechanical Energy and Thermal Energy (PSSC), 16mm b/w, 22 min., MLA

The Nature of Heat, 16mm, b/w, 11 min., Coronet

The Ideal Gas Law; Boyle's Law; Maxwell-Boltzmann Distribution; Avogadro's Principle; Temperature, Energy, and Thermal Equilibrium; Charles' Law; Graham's Law, S8 or 16mm, color, 3-4 min. each, Kalmia

Laboratory:
Bernard and Epp: #17: Pressure and Volume Relations for a Gas

Computer Resources for Chapter 17

Programs:

1. *Physics Vol. 6: Thermodynamics*. Cross. Apple II. Tutorial programs on calorimetry, p-V, p-T, and V-T diagrams, thermodynamic cycles, heat engines, and molecular motion. Reviewed TPT April 1985.

2. *Animation Demonstration: Animated Particles*. Conduit. Apple II. Illustra-tions for kinetic theory lectures. The influence of gravitational and magnetic fields are also simulated. Reviewed TPT November 1986.

3. *Physics Simulations III: Gas*. Kinko's. An excellent simulation of gas molecules in a box. Use for illustration of lectures.

Computer Notes:

CHAPTER 17: LECTURE NOTES
THE IDEAL GAS LAW AND KINETIC THEORY

Introduction (p. 348)

Molecular Mass, the Mole, and Avogadro's Number (p. 349)

Atomic and Molecular Masses

The Mole and Avogadro's Number

The Ideal Gas Law and the Behavior of Gases (p. 351)

The Ideal Gas Law

CHAPTER 17: LECTURE NOTES

Boyle's Law

Charles' Law

Dalton's Law of Partial Pressures

Kinetic Theory of Gases (p. 356)

The Distribution of Molecular Speeds

Kinetic Theory

CHAPTER 17: LECTURE NOTES

The Internal Energy of a Monatomic Ideal Gas

Diffusion (p. 360)

CHAPTER 17: NEXT TIME NOTES

CHAPTER 18: TEACHING AIDS

THEMODYNAMICS: THE ZEROTH LAW AND THE FIRST LAW

Transparencies:
Figure 18.8: Isothermal expansion of an ideal gas.
Figure 18.9: Adiabatic expansion of an ideal gas.

Solved Problems:
Text Problem 7 is Study Guide Practice Problem 3.

Spreadsheet:
#34: Atmospheric Pressure

Demonstrations:
Freier and Anderson He-1 - 6;
Meiners 26-4.1, 26-4.5, 26-4.6

1. "Boyled" Marshmallow: This demonstration appeared on the scene about ten years ago--at least that's when I learned about it. Place a marshmallow under a bell jar and pump to get a decent vacuum. Observe the rather spectacular change that occurs when air is admitted into the jar. A couple of suggestions: Illuminate the bell jar so that the class can see what's going on. Another possibility is to construct a small plexiglas chamber with a pump-out and place it on an overhead projector so students can get a really good view.

Films:
Perpetual Motion, 16mm, color, 11 min., BFA
Mechanical Equivalent of Heat, 16mm b/w, 30 min., EBEC

Laboratory:
Preston: #12: Mechanical Equivalent of Heat

Computer Resources for Chapter 18

Programs:

1. *Physics Vol. 6: Thermodynamics*. Cross. Apple II. Tutorial programs on calorimetry, p-V, p-T, and V-T diagrams, thermodynamic cycles, heat engines, and molecular motion. Reviewed TPT April 1985.

Computer Notes:

CHAPTER 18: LECTURE NOTES

THERMODYNAMICS: THE ZEROTH LAW AND THE FIRST LAW

Introduction (p. 368)

The Zeroth Law of Thermodynamics (p. 369)

The First Law of Thermodynamics (p. 370)

Thermal Processes Involving Pressure, Volume, and Temperature (p. 372)

    Isobaric Processes

CHAPTER 18: LECTURE NOTES

Isochoric Processes

Isothermal Processes

Adiabatic Processes

Thermal Processes That Utilize an Ideal Gas (p. 374)

Isothermal Expansion or Compression

Adaibatic Expansion or Compression

CHAPTER 18: LECTURE NOTES

Specific Heat Capacities and the First Law of Thermodynamics (p. 377)

Latent Heats and the First Law of Thermodynamics (p. 379)

CHAPTER 18: NEXT TIME NOTES

CHAPTER 19: TEACHING AIDS

THERMODYNAMICS: THE SECOND LAW AND THE THIRD LAW

Transparencies:
Figure 19.1: A Steam Engine.
Figure 19.8: The hot reservoir and the cold reservoir of a refrigerator.
Figure 19.10: Conventional electric heating system and heat pump.

Solved Problems: None

Spreadsheet:
#35: Heat Engines

Demonstrations:
Freier and Anderson: Hm-1, 2, 5;
Hilton H-5a, b
Comments: This material does not lend itself well to
simple demonstrations. Some teachers have found it useful to
show a cutaway model of a four-cycle internal combustion engine.
Others use small, working model engines--such as an alcohol-fueled
steam engine. A couple of ideas that I've found useful are:

1. Entropy. I put some water in a fairly large beaker. In class I drop some food coloring dye into the water and let the class observe the rather slow mixing. After I shake the beaker to get full mixing, I place the beaker on lecture desk and announce to the class that if the water and the dye separate (i.e., unmix) before the end of the class, there will be no examination in the course.

2. I find that students are interested in the performance ratings of air conditioners and heat pumps. So I discuss these in some detail as time permits.

Films:
Video Vignette: Time Running Backwards
Children at Play (Time reversed sequences), S8, color, 4 min., AAPT
Reversibility of Time, S8, color, 4 min., Kalmia
You Can't Go Back, 16mm, color, 6 min., NCSU

Laboratory: None suggested

Computer Resources for Chapter 19

Programs:

1. *Physics Vol. 6: Thermodynamics*. Cross. Apple II. Tutorial programs on calorimetry, p-V, p-T, and V-T diagrams, thermodynamic cycles, heat engines, and molecular motion. Reviewed TPT April 1985.

Computer Notes:

CHAPTER 19: LECTURE NOTES

THERMODYNAMICS: THE SECOND LAW AND THE THIRD LAW

The Second Law of Thermodynamics (p. 386)

Heat Engines (p. 387)

Introduction

Efficiency

Carnot's Principle (p. 389)

Reversible Processes

The Statement of Carnot's Principle

152

CHAPTER 19: LECTURE NOTES

The Efficiency of the Carnot Heat Engine (p. 392)

Refrigerators, Air Conditioners, and Heat Pumps (p. 394)

Entropy and the Second Law of Thermodynamics (p. 397)
Introduction

Entropy

CHAPTER 19: LECTURE NOTES

Entropy and Energy That is Unavailable for Doing Work

Order and Disorder

The Third Law of Thermodynamics (p. 401)

CHAPTER 19: NEXT TIME NOTES

CHAPTER 20: TEACHING AIDS

AN INTRODUCTION TO WAVES

Transparencies:
Figure 20.2: Generating a transverse wave on a Slinky.
Figure 20.3: Generating a longitudinal wave on a Slinky.
Figure 20.4: A water wave is neither transverse nor longitudinal.

Solved Problems: None

Spreadsheets: None

Demonstrations:
Freier and Anderson Sa-3 - 6, 12 - 14;
Hilton S-2a, c, d;
Meiners 18-3.1

1. Transverse Waves on a String: Attach to one of the side walls of the lecture room a long (10 to 15 ft) rope (or rubber tubing, or coiled telephone cord, or coiled spiral spring). Shake at the free end to send a single pulse along the rope. Discuss the reflected pulse. Then attach a small flashlight bulb (wired to a small battery). Turn off the room lights and generate another pulse. The up and down transverse motion of the light is clearly evident. Move the free end up and down to generate standing waves. SUGGESTION: Save the full demonstration and discussion of transverse standing waves for Chapter 22.

Films:
Video Vignette: The Guitar String
Simple Waves (PSSC), 16mm, b/w, 27 min., MLA
Pulses and Waves; Single Pulses in a String (Baez), S8, color, 4 min. each, EBEC

Laboratory:
Bernard and Epp: #22: A Study of Vibrating Strings
Preston: #21: Waves

Computer Resources for Chapter 20

Projects:

1. Have students use *Eureka*, a spreadsheet, or their own computer programs to investigate energy in a string carrying a wave. The program should calculate the kinetic, potential, and total energies at a given point and time, given the string displacement as a function of position and time. Use the program to plot the energies as functions of time for a given position. Consider a pulse, a sinusoidal wave, and a standing wave. Demonstrate that energy passes the point in the first two cases but not in the third.

Computer Notes:

CHAPTER 20: LECTURE NOTES
AN INTRODUCTION TO WAVES

The Nature of Waves (p. 410)

Transverse Waves

Longitudinal Waves

Periodic Waves (p. 412)

Amplitude

Wavelength

Period

Frequency

CHAPTER 20: LECTURE NOTES

The Speed of a Wave on a String (p. 414)

The Dependence of Wave Speed on Properties of the String

Derivation of Formula for Speed of a Wave on a String

CHAPTER 20: LECTURE NOTES

The Mathematical Description of a Wave (p. 414)

CHAPTER 20: NEXT TIME NOTES

CHAPTER 21: TEACHING AIDS
SOUND

Transparencies:
Figure 21.4: A sound wave is a series of alternating condensations and rarefactions.

Figure 21.15: The Doppler effect.

Solved Problems:
Text Problem 31 is Study Guide Example 5.

Spreadsheet:
#24: Doppler Shift

Demonstrations:

Demonstrations in Acoustics:	A 3/4" color videocassette. Has 29 demonstrations in acoustics. Order from: Department of Physics, University of Maryland, College Park, MD 20742.

Beats: Freier and Anderson Si-4 - 6;
Hilton S-5;
Meiners 19-5.4, 19-5.5

Doppler: Freier and Anderson Si-1 - 3;
Hilton S-6;
Meiners 19-6.1, 19-6.2

Speed of Sound: Freier and Anderson Sh-1, 2;
Hilton S-3f, g

Human Ear: Freier and Anderson Sh-3, Sl-1

1. Singing Glass: Use a thin-walled glass; an inexpensive wine goblet works well; fine crystal works better--but I don't use it. Fill about half-full with water. Dip your large finger into the water, and move the finger around the rim of the glass, using a moderate pressure. It's important to move thefinger at a nearly contant rate; jerking and stopping give poor results. With a little practice, you'll produce a pleasant tone that is easily heard in a large lecture hall. Note the intricate standing waves on the water.

Films:
A Look at Sound, 16mm or 3/4" videocassette, color, 30 min., TIME

The Science of Musical Sounds, 16mm color, 11 min., ACAY

Sound Waves in Air (PSSC), 16mm, b/w, 35 min., MLA

Propagation of Waves II: Standing Waves and the Doppler Effect, S8, color,
4 min., DEGR

Laboratory:

Bernard and Epp: #24: Velocity of Sound in a Metal -- Kundt's-Tube Method

Computer Resources for Chapter 21

Programs:

1. *Animation Demonstration: Animated Waves*. Conduit. Apple II.

2. *The microcomputer Based Lab Project Sound*. HRM. Sound is picked up by a microphone and intensity is plotted as a function of time on the monitor screen. Use this as an alternative to an oscilloscope. It has the advantages that sound patterns can be stored on disk and recalled for later use and two patterns can be displayed simultaneously for comparison. Any portion of a pattern can be magnified for closer study.

3. *Phys. Software Lib*. Disk 14: Acoustics. Allyn and Bacon. Apple II. Tutorial

Computer Notes:

CHAPTER 21: LECTURE NOTES
SOUND

The Nature of Sound (p. 421)

Longitudinal Sound Waves

Frequency of A Sound Wave

The Pressure Amplitude of A Sound Wave

The Speed of Sound (p. 424)

Gases

Liquids

Solid Bars

Sound Intensity (p. 426)

CHAPTER 21: LECTURE NOTES

Decibels (p. 428)

Comparing Sound Intensities Using Decibels

Intensity Level Changes and Loudness Changes

Applications of Sound (p. 431)

Sonar

Ultrasound in Medicine

Ultrasonic Cleaners

The Doppler Effect (p. 433)

Introduction

Moving Source

CHAPTER 21: LECTURE NOTES

Moving Observer

General Case

Doppler Flow Meter

The Human Ear (p. 439)

Physiology of the Ear

Sensitivity of the Ear

CHAPTER 21: NEXT TIME NOTES

CHAPTER 22: TEACHING AIDS
THE PRINCIPLE OF LINEAR SUPERPOSITION AND INTERFERENCE PHENOMENA

Transparencies:
Figure 22.3: Constructive interference between waves from two hi-fi speakers.
Figure 22.5: Destructive interference between waves from two hi-fi speakers.
Figure 22.13: A 10-Hz sound wave combines with a 12-Hz sound wave to produce a wave with a beat frequency of 2 Hz.

Solved Problems: None

Spreadsheets:
#20: The Tacoma Narrows Bridge
#23: Singing Rods

Demonstrations:
Standing Transverse Waves: Freier and Anderson Sa-8;
                                Hilton S-4b;
                                Meiners 18-5.6, 18-5.7, 18-7.1
Standing Longitudinal Waves: Freier and Anderson Sa-17, 18, Se-1 - 5, 8 - 11;
                                Hilton S-2h, S-4c;
                                Meiners 19-3.1, 19-3.3, 19-3.4, 19-3.5
Two Dimensional Waves: Freier and Anderson Sb-1, 2, 3;
                                Meiners 19-4.1, 19-4.12
Harmonics: Freier and Anderson Sj-2 - 6;
              Hilton S-7a, b, c, d, f
Interference in Sound: Freier and Anderson Sl-3;
                            Meiners 19-4.10, 19-5.2

Films:
Standing Waves and the Principle of Superposition, 16mm or videocassette, color, 11 min., EBEC

The Music of Sound, 16mm, color, 15 min., Pyramid

Propagation of Waves III: Interference, S8, color, 7 min., DEGR

Standing Waves on a String; Standing Waves in a Gas; Vibrations of a Drum; Vibrations of a Metal Plate; Vibrations of a Rubber Hose; Tacoma Narrows Bridge Collapse, S8, color, 3-4 min. each, Kalmia

Dynamic response of a Suspension Bridge, S8, color, 3.5 min., AAPT

Laboratory:

Bernard and Epp: #23: Velocity of Sound in Air--Resonance-Tube Method
#24: Velocity of Sound in a Metal--Kundt's-Tube Method

Computer Resources for Chapter 22

Programs:

1. *Physics Disk 2: Waves.* 6502. Apple II. Simulations useful for lectures include the reflection of a pulse at a fixed and at a free end of a string, superposition of two sine waves, standing waves, and beats. Reviewed TPT September 1986.

2. *Wave Addition II.* Vernier. Apple II. Simulation of the addition of two waves. In some segments the user chooses the parameters of the second wave. Useful as a lecture demonstration of beats and interference effects. Can also be used to demonstrate Fourier synthesis of sawtooth, square, and triangular waves. Reviewed TPT February 1986.

3. *Animation Demonstration: Animated Waves.* Conduit. Apple II. Simulations which can be used to illustrate lectures on standing waves, traveling pulses, Doppler effect for sound, group velocity, and relativistic e-m waves. Reviewed TPT November 1986.

Interactive Videodisk:

1. The Puzzle of the Tacoma Narrows Bridge Collapse by R.G. Fuller, D.A. Zollman, and T.C. Campbell. Wiley. This videodisk shows the film of the collapse of the bridge. It allows the students to select various demonstration experiments, which are then shown and used to investigate standing waves, resonance phenomena, and the effect of wind on the bridge.

Computer Notes:

CHAPTER 22: LECTURE NOTES
THE PRINCIPLE OF LINEAR SUPERPOSITION AND INTERFERENCE PHENOMENA

The Principle of Linear Superposition (p. 445)

Constructive and Destructive Interference of Sound Waves (p. 447)

Constructive Interference

Destructive Interference

Interference--The General Picture

170

CHAPTER 22: LECTURE NOTES

Diffraction (p. 450)

Beats (p. 452)

Transverse Standing Waves (p. 454)

Generating Standing Waves

Resonance and Standing Waves

CHAPTER 22: LECTURE NOTES

Longitudinal Standing Waves (p. 458)

The Nature of a Longitudinal Standing Wave

Longitudinal Standing Waves in Air Columns

Complex Sound Waves (p. 461)

CHAPTER 22: NEXT TIME NOTES

CHAPTER 23: TEACHING AIDS

ELECTRIC FORCES AND ELECTRIC FIELDS

Transparencies:

Figure 23.3: Unlike charges attract each other; like charges repel each other.
Figure 23.22: The electric field lines in the vicinity of an electric dipole.
Figure 23.23: The electric field lines for two identical positive charges.
Figure 23.27: (a) The essential elements of a copying machine.
(b) The five steps in the xerographic process.

Solved Problems:

Text Problem 21 is Study Guide Example 5.
Text Problem 1 is Study Guide Practice Problem 1.
Text Problem 25 is Study Guide Practice Problem 6.

Spreadsheets: None

Demonstrations:

Charging and Electroscopes:	Freier and Anderson Ea-1, 2, 11;
	Hilton E-1a - f
Electrostatic Force:	Freier and Anderson Ea-5, 6, 8, 12, 15, 17, Eb-3, 4,
	9, 10, 12, Ec-4, 5, 6;
	Hilton E-5b;
	Meiners 29-1.4, 29-1.9, 29-1.18, 29-1.23
Induced Charges:	Freier and Anderson Ea-12, 13, 14;
	Hilton E-1g
Lines of Force:	Freier and Anderson Eb-1, Ec-2, 3, 4;
	Meiners 29-2.1

Films

Coulomb's Law (PSSC), 16mm, b/w, 30 Min., MLA
Coulomb Force Constant, 16mm, b/w, 34 min., MLA
Electric Fields (PSSC), 16mm, b/w, 24 min., MLA
Electrostatic Charges and Forces, 16mm, b/w, 13 min., Coronet
Introduction to Electrostatics; Insulators and Conductors; Electrostatic
    Induction; The Electroscope; Problems in Electrostatics; S8, color,
    4 min. each, Kalmia
Coulomb's Law; Discharging the Electroscope: Conduction and Ionization;
    Electric Field and Induced Charges; Electrostatic Attraction; Electrostatic
    Repulsion; S8, color, 4 min. each., EBEC

Laboratory: None suggested

Computer Resources for Chapter 23

Programs:

1. *Basic Concepts of Electricity, Series I: Basic Concepts.* Merlan. Apple II+, IIe. Introduction and drill on charging by rubbing, current in simple circuits, electric potential difference. Reviewed TPT November 1983.

2   *Physics Simulations II: Coulomb.* Kinko's. Macintosh. User gives up to 15 charges and their positions, then the program displays electric field lines.

Projects:

1. Have students use *Eureka* or write programs to calculate the electric fields of discrete charge distributions. Have them use the program to plot the magnitude of the field at various distances from a dipole along lines that are perpendicular and parallel to the dipole moment.

Computer Notes:

CHAPTER 23: LECTURE NOTES
ELECTRIC FORCES AND ELECTRIC FIELDS

The Origin of Electricity (p. 468)

Charged Objects and the Electric Forces Between Them (p. 469)

The Separation of Charges

The Conservation of Charge

The Electric Force Between Charges

Conductors and Insulators (p. 470)

Charging by Contact and by Induction (p. 471)

Charging by Contact

Charging by Induction

CHAPTER 23: LECTURE NOTES

The Electroscope

Coulomb's Law (p. 473)

The Force Between Two Point Charges--Coulomb's Law

The Force on a Point Charge due to Two or More Other Point Charges

The Electric Field (p. 477)

Definition of the Electric Field

Electric Fields Produced by Point Charges

CHAPTER 23: LECTURE NOTES

THE ELECTRIC FIELD PRODUCED BY A PARALLEL PLATE CAPACITOR

Electric Field Lines (p. 481)

The Electric Field Inside a Conductor: Shielding (p. 484)

Applications of Electrostatics (p. 486)

    Xerography

    Laser Printer

    Inkjet Printers

    Electrostatic Cleaner

CHAPTER 23: NEXT TIME NOTES

CHAPTER 24: TEACHING AIDS

ELECTRIC POTENTIAL ENERGY AND ELECTRIC POTENTIAL

Transparencies:

Figure 24.4: An external agent does positive work in moving a positive test charge q_o closer to a positive charge q.

Figure 24.15: The electric field lines inside an empty capacitor and inside a capacitor filled with a dielectric.

Solved Problems:

Text Problem 11 is Study Guide Practice Problem 2.

Spreadsheet:

#36: Electric Potential Near Electrons

Demonstrations:

Charges on Conductors: Freier and Anderson Ea-7, 18, 23, Eb-7;
                            Hilton E-1h;
                            Meiners 29-2.8

Electrostatic Generators: Freier and Anderson Ea-22, Ec-1;
                            Hilton E-1i, j;
                            Meiners 29-1.25, 29-1.26

Capacitors: Freier and Anderson Eb-8, Ed-1, 2, 3, 4, 7, 8;
               Hilton E-4b, c, d;
               Meiners 29-4.1, 29-4.13

Films:

Video Vignette: Flying a Kite in a Storm

Electric Potential Energy & Potential Difference (PSSC), 16mm, b/w, 53 min., MLA

The Faraday Ice-Pail Experiment; Charge Distribution: Concentration and Point
    Discharge; The Van de Graaff Generator; Capacitors and Dielectrics;
    S8, color, 4 min. each, Kalmia

Increasing the Potential of a Capacitor; Polarity; Conductors, Insulators
    and Capacitors; Variation of Charge with Curvature; A Working Model
    of a Van de Graaff Generator; S8, color, 4 min. each, EBEC

Capacitor I: Voltage and Force; Capacitor II: Dipoles and Dielectrics; S8,
    4 min. each, DEGR

Laboratory:

Bernard and Epp: #25: Mapping of Electric Fields
                    #36: The Ocilloscope

Preston: #16: The Ocilloscope

Computer Resources for Chapter 24

Programs:

1. *Physics Disk 3: Electric Fields and Potentials.* 6052. Apple II. Generates field lines and equipotential surfaces for user supplied distribution of discrete charges. Diagrams can be stored for later display. Chiefly for lecture illustrations. Reviewed TPT September 1986.

2. *Laboratory Simulations in Atomic Physics.* Norwalk. Apple II. Simulations of the deflection of an electron by an electric field, the Thompson e/m experiment, the Millikan oil drop experiment, and a mass spectrometer. Parameters are selected by the user. Excellent for illustrating lectures. Some parts can be used in connection with this chapter, some in connection with Chapter 27. Reviewed TPT March 1984.

Computer Notes:

CHAPTER 24: LECTURE NOTES
ELECTRIC POTENTIAL ENERGY AND ELECTRIC POTENTIAL

Potential Energy (p. 495)

Gravitational Potential Energy

Electric Potential Energy

The Electric Potential Difference (p. 496)

The Electric Potential Difference Created by Point Charges (p. 499)

A Single Point Charge

CHAPTER 24: LECTURE NOTES

Potential of Multiple Point Charges

Equipotential Surfaces and Their Relationship to the Electric Field (p. 502)

Equipotential Surfaces

The Relation Between the Electric Field and the Electric Potential

Capacitors and Dielectrics (p. 505) The Capacitance of a Capacitor

The Dielectric Constant

CHAPTER 24: LECTURE NOTES

The Capacitance of a Parallel Plate Capacitor

Energy Stored in a Capacitor

Medical Applications of Electric Potential Differences (p. 510)

CHAPTER 24: NEXT TIME NOTES

CHAPTER 25: TEACHING AIDS
ELECTRIC CIRCUITS: BASIC CONCEPTS

Transparencies:
Figure 25.12: A clothes drier connected to a wall outlet via a two-prong plug.
Figure 25.13: A clothes drier connected to a wall outlet via a three-prong plug

Solved Problems:
Text Problem 19 is Study Guide Example 3.
Text Problem 17 is Study Guide Practice Problem 5.

Spreadsheet:
#37: The Incandescent Light Bulb

Demonstrations:
Ohm's Law: Freier and Anderson Eg-2, Eo-1;
Hilton E-2c
Resistance: Freier and Anderson Eg-1, 3, 6, Eh-3;
Hilton E-3b
Temperature Coefficient of Resistance: Freier and Anderson Eg 4, 5;
Meiners 30-1.4
Emfs: Freier and Anderson Ee-2, 3, 4;
Hilton E-3

1. A Questionable Demonstration on Heating: Connect a resistor to a power supply and adjust the voltage to a level that slightly exceeds the rated power dissipation of the resistor. It soon will begin to smoke. I'm a bit ambivalent on doing this type of experiment, but it does graphically communicate the fact that we often need to know both the resistance and the power rating.

2. Sagging Wire: Suspend a long wire (one capable of handling 20 amps) a few feet above the lecture desk with the wire horizontal and stretched rather tightly. Connect to a high-current power supply. Wire will sag substantially.

Films
Ohm's Law, 16mm, color, 6 min., Coronet
Introduction to the Cathode Ray Oscilloscope, 16mm, color, 11 min., EBEC
An Introduction to the General Purpose Oscilloscope, 16mm, color, 23 min., EDC

Laboratory:
Bernard and Epp: #29: A Study of the Factors Affecting Resistance
#30: The Heating Effect of an Electric Current

Computer Resources for Chapter 25

Programs:

1. *Basic Electricity. Programs.* Apple II. Drill on circuits containing batteries and resistors. Reviewed TPT April 1984.

Computer Notes:

CHAPTER 25: LECTURE NOTES
ELECTRIC CIRCUITS: BASIC CONCEPTS

The Purpose of Electric Circuits (p. 518)

Ohm's Law (p. 520)

Resistance and Resistivity (p. 522)

Dependence of Resistance on Length and Area of Conductor

Dependence of Resistance on Temperature

CHAPTER 25: LECTURE NOTES

Electric Power (p. 524)

Alternating Current (p. 525)

CHAPTER 25: LECTURE NOTES

Safety and the Physiological Effects of Current (p. 529)

CHAPTER 25: NEXT TIME NOTES

CHAPTER 26: TEACHING AIDS
ELECTRIC CIRCUITS: ADDITIONAL CONCEPTS

Transparencies:
Figure 26.7:   Four circuits that are equivalent.
Figure 26.8 A resistor connected to a battery is in series
with the internal resistance of the battery.

Solved Problems:
Text Problem 35 is Study Guide Example 9.

Spreadsheet:
#38: Electric Circuits

Demonstrations:
Resistive Circuits: Freier and Anderson Eh-1, Eo-5, 6, 7;
                         Hilton E-2b, c, E-3a, d
Capacitors: Freier and Anderson Ed-6, 7, 8, Eo-12;
                         Hilton E-4e, f
Power: Freier and Anderson Eh-3, 4;
                         Hilton E-3g
Wheatstone Bridge: Freier and Anderson Eg-6, Eo-8;
                         Hilton E-3b
Potentiometer: Freier and Anderson Eg-7, Eo-3;
                         Hilton E-3c
Kirchhoff's Laws: Freier and Anderson Eo-2
Meters: Freier and Anderson Ej-6, 7

Films:
Electric Fields & Moving Media, 16mm or 3/4" videocassette, color, 32 min., EDC
E.M.F. (PSSC), 16mm, b/w, 19 min., MLA
Series and Parallel Circuits, 16mm, b/w, 11 min., EBEC
Capacitance of Capacitor Combinations: Parallel; Capacitance of Capacitor
    Combinations: Series; S8, color, 4 min. each, EBEC

Laboratory:
Bernard and Epp: #27: Methods of Measuring Resistance
                  #28: Measurements of Potential Difference with a Potentiometer
                  #31: Circuits Containing More Than One Potential Source
                  #32: A Study of Capacitance and Capacitor Transients
Preston: #14: Electricity
                  #15: Ohm's Law: DC & AC Circuits

Computer Resources for Chapter 26

Programs:

1. *Circuit Lab*. Mark. Apple II. One of four basic circuits can be selected. Light bulbs, switches, resistors, ammeters, and voltmeters are placed in the circuit by the user, who also selects values for the circuit elements. Ammeters and voltmeters then show correct values. Use as a drill or to illustrate circuits in lectures. Reviewed TPT April 1986.

Computer Notes:

CHAPTER 26: LECTURE NOTES
ELECTRIC CIRCUITS: ADDITIONAL CONCEPTS

Series Wiring (p. 534)

Parallel Wiring (p. 535)

Circuits That Are Wired Partially in Series and Partially in Parallel (p. 538)

CHAPTER 26: LECTURE NOTES

Internal Resistance (p. 539)

The Measurement of Current, Voltage, and Resistance (p. 540)
   The Galvanometer

The Ammeter

The Voltmeter

The Wheatstone Bridge

CHAPTER 26: LECTURE NOTES

Kirchhoff's Rules (p. 544)

Capacitors in Series and Parallel (p. 546)

RC Circuits (p. 547)

Charging a Capacitor Discharging a Capacitor

CHAPTER 26: NEXT TIME NOTES

CHAPTER 27: TEACHING AIDS

MAGNETIC FORCES AND MAGNETIC FIELDS

Transparencies:

Figure 27.7: Right-hand rule no. 1: Determining the direction of the force on positive charge moving in a magnetic field.

Figure 27.20: Using right-hand rule no. 2 to determine the direction of the magnetic field produced by a long straight wire.

Figure 27.29: Magnetizing the magnetic coating on the tape of a recorder.

Solved Problems:

Text Problem 9 is Study Guide Example 3.

Text Problem 21 is Study Guide Example 4.

Text Problem 35 is Study Guide Example 5.

Text Problem 11 is Study Guide Practice Problem 3.

Spreadsheets:

#39: High Energy Particle Storage Rings

#40: Magnetic Fields Inside a Square Coil

Demonstrations:

Permanent Magnets: Freier and Anderson Er-1, 4 - 9;
Hilton E-6a, b, c, d;
Meiners 32-1.1

Forces on Currents: Freier and Anderson Ei-7, 12, 13, 14, 15, 19, 20;
Hilton E-7a, b, c;
Meiners 31-1.1

Deflection of Electron Beam: Freier and Anderson Ei-18, Ep-8, 11;
Meiners 31-1.8

Meters: Freier and Anderson Ej-1, 2

Magnetic Fields of Currents: Freier and Anderson Ei-8 - 11;
Hilton E-7b, d, E-9b, c;
Meiners 31-1.17, 31-1.19, 31-1.20, 31-1.25

Magnetic Forces Between Wires: Freier and Anderson Ei-1 - 6;
Hilton E-7e, f, g, E-9a;
Meiners 31-1.27

Films:

Magnetic Fields and Electric Currents, I, 16mm, color, 14.5 min., BFA

The Magnetic Field; The Field from a Steady Current; Field vs. Current; Uniform and Non-Uniform Fields, S8, color, 3 min. each, Kalmia

Electromagnetic Induction, 16mm, b/w, 13 min., Coronet

Laboratory:

Bernard and Epp: #33: A Study of Magnetic Fields

#34: Measurement of the Earth's Magnetic Field

Preston: #20: Electron Orbits in a Magnetic Field

Computer Resources for Chapter 27

Programs:

1. *Charged Particle Workshop. High.* Apple II. Shows trajectories of charged particles in a uniform electric field, a uniform magnetic field, and crossed electric and magnetic fields. Velocity components can be displayed. Can be used to illustrate lectures.

2. *Laboratory Simulations in Atomic Physics.* See Chapter 24 notes.

3. *Physics Simulations II: Ampere.* Kinko's. Macintosh. Positions and currents of up to 9 coaxial loops are specified by the user, then the program displays magnetic field lines. Use to illustrate lectures.

Computer Notes:

CHAPTER 27: LECTURE NOTES
MAGNETIC FORCES AND MAGNETIC FIELDS

Magnets and Magnetic Fields (p. 557)

Permanent Magnets

The Magnetic Field

Geomagnetism

The Force That a Magnetic Field Exerts on a Moving Charge (p. 561)

The Nature of the Magnetic Force

CHAPTER 27: LECTURE NOTES

Definition of the Magnetic Field

The Motion of Charged Particles in a Magnetic Field (p. 563)

Comparing the Motion in Electric and Magnetic Fields

The Work Done on a Charged Particle Moving Through Electric and Magnetic Fields

The Circular Trajectory

CHAPTER 27: LECTURE NOTES

The Mass Spectrometer and the Hall Effect (p. 566)

The Mass Spectrometer

The Hall Effect

The Force on a Current in a Magnetic Field (p. 568)

The Torque on a Current-Carrying Coil (p. 570)

The General Picture

CHAPTER 27: LECTURE NOTES

The Galvanometer

The Direct-Current Electric Motor

Magnetic Fields Produced by Currents (p. 574)

The Magnetic Field Produced by a Long, Straight Current-Carrying Wire

The Magnetic Field Produced by a Loop of Wire

CHAPTER 27: LECTURE NOTES

The Solenoid

Magnetic Materials (p. 580)

Ferromagnetism

Induced Magnetism

Magnetic Tape Recording

Operational Definitions of the Ampere and the Coulomb (p. 583)

CHAPTER 27: NEXT TIME NOTES

CHAPTER 28: TEACHING AIDS

ELECTROMAGNETIC INDUCTION

Transparencies:

Figure 28.7: Side view of a rectangular coil oriented at three different angles to a magnetic field.

Figure 28.12: A vibrating string of an electric guitar induces an emf in the coil of the pickup.

Solved Problems:

Text Problem 31 is Study Guide Example 8.

Spreadsheet:

#41: Startup Current in an Electric Motor

Demonstrations:

Induced Currents: Freier and Anderson Ek-3 - 6;
Hilton E-8a;
Meiners 31-2.1

Generators: Freier and Anderson Eq-4, 5, 7, Er-1;
Hilton E-8b, c;
Meiners 31-2.15

Eddy Currents: Freier and Anderson El-1 - 6;
Hilton E-8d;
Meiners 31-2.6, 31-2.7

Transformers: Freier and Anderson Em-2, 4, 5, 10, Ep-2;
Hilton E-11a, b, c, e;
Meiners 31-2.2, 31-3.6

Forces due to Induced Currents: Freier and Anderson Eh-1,2, Em-12,13;
Meiners 31-2.9

Inductance: Freier and Anderson Ek-7, Em-1, 8, En-5, 6, 7, Eo-11, Eq-1;
Hilton E-12a, b, c, d;
Meiners 31-3.2

Films:

Electromagnetic Induction, 16mm, b/w, 13 min., Coronet The
Concept of a Changing Flux; Faraday's Law of Induction, S8,
color, 3 min. each, Kalmia
Lenz's Law; Large Inductance: Current Buildup, S8, color, 3 min each, AAPT

Laboratory:

Bernard and Epp: #35: Electromagnetic Induction

Computer Resources for Chapter 28

Programs:

1. *Faraday's Law. Microphys.* Apple II. A basic tutorial on induced emfs.
2. *Faraday's Law and Inductance.* Allyn and Bacon. Apple II. Useful for self-study by students.

Computer Notes:

CHAPTER 28: LECTURE NOTES
ELECTROMAGNETIC INDUCTION

Induced Emf and Induced Current (p. 592)

Motional Emf (p. 595)

The Emf Induced in a Moving Conductor

Motional Emf and Electrical Energy

Magnetic Flux (p. 598)

Motional Emf and Magnetic Flux

CHAPTER 28: LECTURE NOTES

A General Expression for Magnetic Flux

Graphical Interpretation of Magnetic Flux

Faraday's Law of Electromagnetic Induction (p. 600)

Lenz's Law (p. 602)

The Polarity of the Induced Emf

CHAPTER 28: LECTURE NOTES

Applications of Electromagnetic Induction: Reproduction of Sound (p. 604)

The Electric Guitar Pickup

The Magnetic Phono Cartridge

The Playback Head of a Tape Deck

The Electric Generator (p. 607)

How a Generator Produces an Emf

The Electrical Energy Delivered by a Genrator and the Countertorque

CHAPTER 28: LECTURE NOTES

The Back Emf Generated by an Electric Motor

Mutual Inductance and Self-Inductance (p. 611)

Mutual Inductance

Self-Inductance

The Energy Stored in an Inductor

CHAPTER 28: LECTURE NOTES

Transformers (p. 615)

CHAPTER 28: NEXT TIME NOTES

CHAPTER 29: TEACHING AIDS
ALTERNATING CURRENT CIRCUITS

Transparencies:
Figure 29.10: Impedance varies with frequency in a series RCL-circuit.
Figure 29.18: Oscillation of a mass on a spring is analogous to the oscillation of the electric and magnetic fields that occur, respectively, in a capacitor and in an inductor.

Solved Problems:
Text Problem 11 is Study Guide Practice Problem 4.
Text Problem 15 is Study Guide Practice Problem 5.
Text Problem 37 is Study Guide Practice Problem 7.

Spreadsheets:
#42: Causing Spark Plugs to Fire
#43: Tuning Your Radio

Demonstrations:
Capacitive Resistance: Freier and Anderson En-4
Inductive Reactance: Freier and Anderson En-3, 5
Impedance: Freier and Anderson Eo-9
Series RCL-Circuit: Freier and Anderson En-1, 2, 12, Eo-13; Hilton E-13a
Resonance: Hilton E-13b, c, e
Capacitors and Inductors in Hi-Fi: Meiners 33-2.5, 33-2.6

Films:
Electromagnetic Oscillator I: Free Oscillations, S8, color, 3 min., DEGR
Electromagnetic Oscillator II: Forced Oscillations, S8, color, 7 min., DEGR
Brattain on Semiconductor Physics, 16mm, b/w, 30 min., BTL
Minority Carriers in Semiconductors, 16mm, b/w, 26 min., EDC

Laboratory:
Bernard and Epp: #37: A Study of Alternating Current Circuits
Preston: #17: AC Behavior of Resistors, Capacitors and Inductors; Resonance

Computer Resources for Chapter 29

Programs:

1. *Apple Physics Disk 1: RCL Circuits.* 6502. Apple II.
2. *Phys. Software Lib. Disk 32: Altenating Currents and Disk 34: RCL Series Circuit.* Allyn and Bacon. Apple II.

Computer Notes:

CHAPTER 29: LECTURE NOTES
ALTERNATING CURRENT CIRCUITS

Capacitors and Capacitive Reactance (p. 626)

Inductors and Inductive Reactance (p. 630)

216

CHAPTER 29: LECTURE NOTES

The Series RCL-Circuit (p. 632)

The Role of Capacitors and Inductors in the Design of Hi-Fi Loudspeakers (p. 635)

Resonance in Electric Circuits (p. 637)

CHAPTER 29: LECTURE NOTES

Semiconductor Devices (p. 640)

n-Type and p-Type Semiconductors

The Semiconductor Diode

Transistors

Integrated Circuits

CHAPTER 29: NEXT TIME NOTES

CHAPTER 30: TEACHING AIDS

ELECTROMAGNETIC WAVES

Transparencies:

Figure 30.3:   The electric field **E** and the magnetic field **B** of an electromagnetic wave traveling along the x axis.

Figure 30.6:   The electromagnetic spectrum.

Solved Problems:

Text Problem 35 is Study Guide Practice Problem 8.

Spreadsheets:

#44: Doppler Radar Speed Measurements

#45: The Brightness of Light On My Desk

Demonstrations:

Radiation: Freier and Anderson Ep-4, 5, 12, 13

Speed of Light: Freier and Anderson Oa-4

Polarization: Freier and Anderson Om-1, 2, 7 - 11, 14 - 19, On-2;
Hilton O8-a,b,c;
Meiners 35-6.2, 35-6.4

1.   Microwaves; Microwave demonstration (or experiment) sets are available from
several science supply firm (PASCO, CENCO, etc). I suggest that any extensive
demonstrations be saved for the optics section--except that a few demonstrations
on polarized microwaves will help students understand the topics discussed in this
section of the chapter. Polarization of light is covered in this chapter. Using
both microwaves and light to demonstrate polarization will help the student to see
the unity of electromagnetic waves. Excellent and simple demonstrations of
polarized light are listed above.

Films:

Electromagnetic Waves (PSSC), 16mm, b/w, 33 min., MLA

Standing Electromagmetic Waves, S8, color, 3 min., EAL

Measurement of the Speed of Light, 16mm, b/w, 7 min., MCGH

Speed of Light (PSSC), 16mm, b/w, 21 min., MLA

Polarization of Light, 16mm, color or b/w, 11 min., EBEC

Polarization, S8, color, 4 min., EBEC

Laboratory:

Bernard and Epp: #46: Polarized Light

Preston: #23: Polarization

Computer Resources for Chapter 30

Programs:

1. *Physics Simulations II: Radiation*. Kinko's. Macintosh. Shows electric field lines of an accelerating charge in linear, circular, or oscillatory motion. User selects the velocity and can view either the near or far field.

Computer Notes:

CHAPTER 30: LECTURE NOTES
ELECTROMAGNETIC WAVES

The Nature of Electromagnetic Waves (p. 651)

The Electromagnetic Spectrum (p. 655)

CHAPTER 30: LECTURE NOTES

The Speed of Light (p. 656)

Experimental Determination of the Speed of Light

Theoretical Prediction of the Speed of Light

The Energy Carried by Electromagnetic Waves (p. 658)

CHAPTER 30: LECTURE NOTES

Polarization (p. 660)

Polarized Electromagnetic Waves

Malus' Law

The Occurrence of Polarized Light in Nature

CHAPTER 30: NEXT TIME NOTES

CHAPTER 31: TEACHING AIDS

THE REFLECTION OF LIGHT AND MIRRORS

Transparencies:

Figure 31.16: Image formation by a concave mirror when the object is placed (a) between the focal point and the center of curvature an (b) beyond the center of curvature.

Figure 31.17: (a) Image formation when an object is placed between the focal point and a concave mirror. (b) A make-up mirror.

Figure 31.18: Ray diagram for a convex mirror showing formation of a virtual image.

Solved Problems:

Text Problem 1 is Study Guide Example 1.

Text Problem 19 is Study Guide Practice Problem 5.

Spreadsheets: None

Demonstrations:

Plane Mirrors: Freier and Anderson Ob-1 - 11;
                   Hilton O-c, d;
                   Meiners 34-1.1

Spherical Mirrors: Freier and Anderson Oc-1 - 11;
                   Hilton O-1e, f

1. Microwaves: See comments on demonstrations in Chapter 30. Using the microwave demonstration apparatus to show reflection (and, for subsequent chapters, to show refraction, diffraction, etc) is very effective. I'd suggest, however, that most demonstrations be done with visible light.

2. Corner Mirrors: My students enjoy looking at images (especially of themselves) formed by two perpendicular mirrors that abut each other. These are easily constructed using 12" x 12" mirror tile mounted onto quarter inch plywood. The third image, the one behind the corner, is reversed left-to-right relative to the image formed by each of the mirrors acting separately. This helps the student to understand what a single plane mirror reverses.

Films:

Introduction to Optics (PSSC), 16mm, color, 23 min., MLA

Sunshine Optics, S8, color, 3.5 min, AAPT

Laboratory:

Bernard and Epp: #38: Reflection and Refraction of Light (the Reflection Part)
                    #39: The Focal Length of a Concave Mirror

Computer Resources for Chapter 31

Programs:

1. *Optics: Mirrors and Beams*. HRM. Apple II. Tutorial on law of reflection.

Computer Notes:

CHAPTER 31: LECTURE NOTES
THE REFLECTION OF LIGHT AND MIRRORS

Wavefronts and Rays (p. 670)

The Reflection of Light (p. 671)

The Formation of Images by a Plane Mirror (p. 672)

CHAPTER 31: LECTURE NOTES

Spherical Mirrors (p. 674)

The Formation of Images by Spherical Mirrors (p. 676)

Image Formation by a Concave Mirror

Image Formation by a Convex Mirror

CHAPTER 31: LECTURE NOTES

The Mirror Equation and the Magnification Equation (p. 679)

Concave Mirrors

Convex Mirrors

Summary of Sign Conventions

CHAPTER 31: NEXT TIME NOTES

CHAPTER 32: TEACHING AIDS
THE REFRACTION OF LIGHT AND LENSES

Transparencies:
Figure 32.20: The optical system of (a) a camera and (b) a projector.
Figure 32.21: Formation of a virtual image by a converging lens.
Figure 32.22: Ray diagram for a converging lens forming a real image.

Solved Problems: None

Spreadsheet:
#47: Simple Lenses

Demonstrations:
Refraction at a Plane Surface: Freier and Anderson Od-1 - 7;
                                                        Meiners 34-1.8
Prisms: Freier and Anderson Of-1 - 4;
             Hilton O-2b
Lenses: Freier and Anderson Og-1 - 7, 9 - 13;
             Hilton O-4a
Polarization: Freier and Anderson Om-2
Total Internal Reflection: Freier and Anderson Oe-1, 2, 3, 5, 6, 7;
                                               Hilton O-2d, e
Rainbow: Freier and Anderson Oj-10;
                  Meiners 34-1.16
Chromatic Aberration: Freier and Anderson Oj-9
Cylindrical Lens: Hilton O-4c

Films:
Reflection and Refraction, 16mm, b/w, 17 min., UEVA
Light and Lenses, 16mm, color, 10 min., JF
Transmission and Reflection; Total Internal Reflection; Refraction;
      The Index of Refraction; S8, color, 4 min. each, EBEC
Sunsets and Scattered Light, S8, color, 3 min, AAPT

Laboratory:
Bernard and Epp: #38: Reflection and Refraction of Light
                                   #40: Properties of Converging and Diverging Lenses
                                   #43: Index of Refraction with the Prism Spectrometer

Computer Resources for Chapter 32

Programs:

1. *Optics and Light*. Focus. Apple II. Demonstration and tutorial on Snell's law and thin lenses. User selects the parameters, then the program draws a ray diagram. Reviewed TPT January 1985.

Computer Notes:

CHAPTER 32: LECTURE NOTES
THE REFRACTION OF LIGHT AND LENSES

The Index of Refraction (p. 686)

The Refraction of Light and Snell's Law (p. 687)

Snell's Law

Apparent Depth

CHAPTER 32: LECTURE NOTES

The Displacement of Light by A Transparent Slab of Material (p. 690)

Derivation of Snell's Law

Total Internal Reflection (p. 692)

The Critical Angle and Total Internal Reflection

Prisms and Total Internal Reflection

CHAPTER 32: LECTURE NOTES

Fiber Optics

Polarization and the Reflection and Refraction of Light (p. 696)

The Dispersion of Light: Prisms and Rainbows (p. 697)

Converging and Diverging Lenses (p. 698)

Converging Lenses

CHAPTER 32: LECTURE NOTES

Diverging Lenses

The Formation of Images by Converging and Diverging Lenses (p. 700)

Ray Diagrams

Image Formation by a Converging Lens

Image Formation by a Diverging Lens

CHAPTER 32: LECTURE NOTES

The Thin-Lens Equation and the Magnification Equation (p. 703)

Lenses in Combination (p. 705)

238

CHAPTER 32: NEXT TIME NOTES

CHAPTER 33: TEACHING AIDS

OPTICAL INSTRUMENTS

Transparencies:
Figure 33.5:   When a suitable diverging lens is used, the image of a distant object is formed on the retina of a nearsighted person.

Figure 33.6:   When a suitable converging lens is used, the image of a nearby object is formed on the retina of a farsighted person.

Solved Problems:
Text Problem 17 is Study Guide Example 6.

Text Problem 29 is Study Guide Example 8.

Text Problem 11 is Study Guide Practice Problem 3.

Text Problem 37 is Study Guide Practice Problem 5.

Text Problem 33 is Study Guide Practice Problem 10.

Spreadsheet:
#46: Human Vision

Demonstrations:
Human Eye: Freier and Anderson Og-8, Oi-10, 11, 12;

Hilton O-5b;

Meiners 34-2.1

Pinhole Camera: Freier and Anderson Oa-2, 3;

Meiners 34-1.10

Camera: Hilton O-5a

Fish-Eye Camera: Meiners 34-1.11, 34-1.12

Telescope: Hilton O-5e, f

Microscope: Hilton O-5c

Films:
Light: Lenses and Optical Instruments, 16mm, bw, 14 min., Coronet

Lens Aberrations, I and II, S8 with 35-mm slides, color, 10.5 min. total, DEGR

The Eyes Have It - Or Do They?, 16mm, color, BFA

Image Formation in the Microscope, S8 and 35-mm slides, color, 5 min., DEGR

The Eye: An Inside Story, 16mm, color, 10 min., Coronet

Laboratory:
Bernard and Epp: #41: Optical Instruments Employing Two Lenses

Preston: #24: Lenses and Microscope

Computer Resources for Chapter 33

Programs:

1. *General Physics Series Volume 8--Optics*. Cross. Apple II. Tutorial.

Computer Notes:

CHAPTER 33: LECTURE NOTES
OPTICAL INSTRUMENTS

The Camera (p. 714)

The Human Eye (p. 717)

The Anatomy of the Eye

The Optics of the Eye

Nearsightedness

Farsightedness

CHAPTER 33: LECTURE NOTES

The Refractive Power of a Lens--The Diopter

Angular Magnification and the Magnifying Glass (p. 721)

Angular Size

Angular Magnification

The Compound Microscope (p. 724)

CHAPTER 33: LECTURE NOTES

The Telescope (p. 726)

The Astronomical Telescope

Terrestrial Telescopes

Lens Aberrations (p. 729)

Spherical Aberration

Chromatic Aberratiuon

Off-Axis Astigmatism

CHAPTER 33: NEXT TIME NOTES

CHAPTER 34: TEACHING AIDS
INTERFERENCE AND THE WAVE NATURE OF LIGHT

Transparencies:
Figure 34.1: Constructive interference by two waves that are in phase.
Figure 34.2: Destructive interference by two waves that are out of phase.
Figure 34.19: Diffraction of light by a single slit.

Solved Problems:
Text Problem 7 is Study Guide Practice Problem 2.
Text Problem 33 is Study Guide Practice Problem 6.

Spreadsheet:
#48: Double Slit Interference Patterns

Demonstrations:
Double Slit Interference:	Freier and Anderson Ol-4, 5, 9;
	Hilton O-7c;
	Meiners 35-2.1
Single Slit Diffraction:	Freier and Anderson Ol-2, 3, 6, 7;
	Hilton O-7c;
	Meiners 35-3.1
Thin Film Interference:	Freier and Anderson Ol-15 - 18;
	Hilton O-7d, e, f;
	Meiners 35-2.2, 35-2.4
Interferometer:	Freier and Anderson Ol-19, 20;
	Hilton O-2e;
	Meiners 35-2.7
Multiple Slits:	Freier and Anderson Ol-10, 13;
	Hilton O-7g;
	Meiners 25-3.2
Diffraction:	Freier and Anderson Ol-14, 21, 23; O-7g,h,j;
	Meiners 35-3.7

Films:
Interference and Diffraction (PSSC, Ripple Tank), 16mm, b/w, 19 min., MLA
Joseph Fraunhofer: Diffraction, 16mm, color, 16 min., RPI
Introduction to Holography, 16mm color, 17 min., EBEC
Interference in Photon Polarization, 16mm, silent, color, 4 min., EDC
Shadow of a Hole, S8, color, 3.5 min., AAPT
Diffraction--Single Slit; Diffraction--Double Slit; Resolving Power; The
    Michelson Interferometer, S8, color, 4 min. each, Kalmia

Laboratory:
Bernard and Epp: #45: A Study of Spectra with the Grating Spectrometer
#44: The Wavelength of Light
Preston: #22: Diffraction and Resolution
#25: Spectrometer: Balmer Series

Computer Resources for Chapter 34

Programs:

1. *Light Waves*. Educational. Apple II. Simulations of Young's experiment with user selected parameters. Students can view either a graph of the intensity or a simulated intensity pattern.

2. *Physics Simulations III: Diffraction*. Kinko's. Macintosh. Program shows intensity plots for single slits, double slits, and other apertures.

Computer Notes:

CHAPTER 34: LECTURE NOTES
INTERFERENCE AND THE WAVE NATURE OF LIGHT

The Principle of Linear Superposition (p. 736)

Young's Double Slit Experiment (p. 739)

Thin Film Interference (p. 742)

CHAPTER 34: LECTURE NOTES

The Michelson Interferometer (p. 745)

Diffraction (p. 747)

CHAPTER 34: LECTURE NOTES

Resolving Power (p. 752)

The Diffraction Grating (p. 754)

The Interfernece Pattern of a Diffraction Grating

The Grating Spectroscope

Compact Disc Players

X-Ray Diffraction (p. 758)

CHAPTER 34: NEXT TIME NOTES

CHAPTER 35: TEACHING AIDS

SPECIAL RELATIVITY

Transparencies:

Figure 35.3: A light clock.

Figure 35.4: An observer on earth and a moving astronaut measure different time intervals between ticks of the astronaut's light clock.

Solved Problems:

Text Problem 21 is Study Guide Practice Problem 8.

Spreadsheet:

#53: Relativistic Speeds of Electrons in a Linear Accelerator

Demonstrations: None suggested

Films:

Video Vignette: The Relativistic Ride

Relativistic Time Dilation (Paul G. Hewitt), color. 12 min., 16mm from SMITH; Videocassette from BAY

The Ultimate Speed: An Exploration with High Energy Electrons, 16mm, b/w, 38 min., MLA

Time Dilation: An Experiment with Mu-Mesons (PSSC), 16mm, b/w, 36 min, MLA $E = mc^2$,16mm or 3/4" videocassette, color, 28 min., UCMC

Marking Time, 16mm or 3/4" videocassette, 28 min., UCMC

Motion and Time: An Introduction to Einstein's Theory of Relativity, 16mm, color, 11 min., STERLED

Mystery of Time, 16mm, color, 28 min., MIS

A Relativistic Ride, 16mm or S8, color, 4 min., EDC

Powers of Ten (Eames), 16mm or 3/4" videocassette, b/w, 10 min. or 25 min., Pyramid

Laboratory: None suggested

Computer Resources for Chapter 35

Programs:

1. *Physics Simulations I: Einstein.* Kinko's. Macintosh. The screen is split to show the views of events as seen in two frames which are moving relative to each other. Clocks show time intervals between events. Use to demonstrate time dilation, length contraction, twin paradox.

2. *Intermediate Physics Simulations: Relativistic Motion.* Good. Apple II. User adjusts the velocity (in two dimensions) of a moving clock, which ticks at uniform intervals and lays down a marker at each tick. The screen shows the time in the observer's frame and in the rest frame of the clock. Use to demonstrate time dilation, length contraction, twin paradox.

Computer Notes:

CHAPTER 35: LECTURE NOTES
SPECIAL RELATIVITY

Events and Inertial Reference Frames (p. 764)

The Postulates of Special Relativity (p. 765)

The Relativity of Time: Time Dilation (p. 766)

Time Dilation

Proper Time

CHAPTER 35: LECTURE NOTES

Space Travel

Verification of Time Dilation

The Relativity of Length: Length Contraction (p. 771)

The Relativity of Mass: Mass Increase (p. 773)

Mass Increase

CHAPTER 35: LECTURE NOTES

The Speed of Light Is the Ultimate Speed

The Equivalence of Energy and Mass: $E = mc^2$ (p. 774)

The Total Energy of an Object

The Transformation Between Mass and Other Forms of Energy

The Relativistic Addition of Velocities (p. 776)

CHAPTER 35: NEXT TIME NOTES

CHAPTER 36: TEACHING AIDS

PARTICLES AND WAVES

Transparencies:

Figure 36.1: A beam of electrons incident on a double slit forms an interference pattern of bright and dark fringes.

Figure 36.7: Computer simulation of the electron version of Young's double-slit experiment.

Solved Problems:

Text Problem 11 is Study Guide Practice Problem 1.

Spreadsheets:

#51: The Low Temperature Heat Capacity of Metals

#52: The Color of a Hot Filament

Demonstrations:

Photoelectric Effect: Freier and Anderson MPb-1;
                        Hilton A-4b, c;
                        Meiners 38-2.1

Models of Atom: Hilton A-5a, b;
                  Meiners 39-5.1

Electron Diffraction: Hilton A-13b;
                        Meiners 38-7.4

Compton Effect: Meiners 38-3.1, 38-3.2

Films:

Matter Waves (PSSC), 16mm, b/w, 28 min., MLA

Anti-Matter, 16mm, color, 12 min., AEF

Wave-Particle Duality, 16mm, color, 22 min., IFB

Interference of Photons (PSSC), 16mm, b/w, 12 min., MLA

Photoelectric Effect (PSSC), 16mm, color, 27 min., MLA

Photoemission of Electrons, 16mm, b/w, 4 min., UEVA

Photons (PSSC), 16mm, b/w, 18 min., MLA

Pressure of Light (PSSC), 16mm, b/w, 23 min., MLA

The Photoelectric Effect, S8, color, 4 min., Kalmia

Discharging the Electroscope--The Photoelectric Effect, S8, color, 4 min., EBEC

Laboratory:

Bernard and Epp: #45: A Study of Spectra with the Grating Spectrometer

Computer Resources for Chapter 36

Programs:

1. *Atoms and Matter.* Focus. A series of programs that simulate various modern experiments. One plots radiative intensity vs. frequency for a blackbody at a temperature chosen by the user. This display can be used to illustrate the lecture. The tutorial material can be used by the students. Reviewed TPT December 1986.

Computer Notes:

CHAPTER 36: LECTURE NOTES

PARTICLES AND WAVES

The Wave-Particle Duality (p. 782)

Blackbody Radiation and Planck's Constant (p. 783)

Photons and the Photoelectric Effect (p. 784)

CHAPTER 36: LECTURE NOTES

The Momentum of a Photon and the Compton Effect (p. 786)

The de Broglie Wavelength and the Wave Nature of Matter (p. 788)

Particle Waves and Probability (p. 789)

CHAPTER 36: LECTURE NOTES

The Uncertaintly Principle (p. 790)

CHAPTER 36: NEXT TIME NOTES

CHAPTER 37: TEACHING AIDS

THE NATURE OF THE ATOM

Transparencies:
Figure 37.9: The Lyman, Balmer, and Paschen series of lines in the hydrogen atom spectrum correspond to transitions that the electron makes between higher and lower energy levels.
Figure 37.21: A schematic drawing of a helium/neon laser.

Solved Problems:
Text Problem 19 is Study Guide Example 3.
Text Problem 25 is Study Guide Example 4.
Text Problem 37 is Study Guide Practice Problem 6.

Spreadsheet:
#49: Rutherford Scattering

Demonstrations:
Lasers: Hilton A-12
X-rays: Hilton A-2c, d, A-7
Zeeman Effect: Freier and Anderson MPc-1;
Hilton A-20a

Films:
Video Vignette: The Golf Ball
The Hydrogen Atom, 16mm, color, 20 min., MLA
Absorption Spectra, 16mm, color, 3 min., OHSU
Bohr Atom, 16mm, b/w, 30 min., EBEC
Electron Shell Structure, 16mm, b/w, 30 min., EBEC
A New Reality (The Work of Niels Bohr), 16mm, color, 50 min., IFB
Atomic Structure and the Periodic Table, 16mm, color, 11 min., EBEC
X-ray Spectrroscopy, 16mm, color, 26 min., NAVC
Introduction to Lasers, 16mm, color, 17 min., EBEC
Laser: The Light of the Future, 16mm, color, 30 min., INUAVC

Laboratory:
Bernard and Epp: #42: The Laser

Computer Resources for Chapter 37

Programs:

1. *Animation Demonstration: Electron Waves in an Atom.* Conduit. Apple II. Compares classical electron orbits and quantum wave patterns. Shows quantization of orbits by applying boundary conditions and simulates radiative transitions. Reviewed TPT November 1986.

Computer Notes:

CHAPTER 37: LECTURE NOTES
THE NATURE OF THE ATOM

Rutherford Scattering and the Nuclear Atom (p. 797)

Line Spectra (p. 799)

The Bohr Model of the Hydrogen Atom (p. 800)

The Model

The Allowed Energies and Radii of the Bohr Orbits

CHAPTER 37: LECTURE NOTES

Energy Level Diagrams

Prediction of the Line Spectra of the Hydrogen Atom

De Broglie's Explanation of Bohr's Assumption About Angular Momentum (p. 807)

The Quantum Mechanical Picture of the Hydrogen Atom (p. 807)

Quantum Numbers

CHAPTER 37: LECTURE NOTES

Electron Probability Clouds

The Pauli Exclusion Principle and the Periodic Table of the Elements (p. 810)

Multiple-Electron Atoms

A Shorthand Notation for the Electronic Configuration of the Atom

The Periodic Table

X-Rays (p. 814)

The Laser (p. 816)

CHAPTER 37: NEXT TIME NOTES

CHAPTER 38: TEACHING AIDS

NUCLEAR PHYSICS AND RADIOACTIVITY

Transparencies:
Figure 38.1:   The atomic nucleus is approximately spherical and contains protons clustered closely with neutrons.

Figure 38.9:   The half-life of a radioactive decay determined from a graph that shows the number of radioactive nuclei as a function of time.

Solved Problems:
Text Problem 3 is Study Guide Example 1.

Text Problem 43 is Study Guide Pactice Problem 7.

Spreadsheet:
#50: Radioactivity

Demonstrations:
Geiger Counter: Freier and Anderson MPa-2;
Meiners 41-1.1

Radioactivity: Hilton A-15, A-16, A-18;
Meiners 41-1.8, 41-1.9

Cloud Chambers: Hilton A-15b,c;
Meiners 41-3.5, 41-3.6

Films:
The Discovery of Radioactivity, 16mm or 3/4" videocassette, color, 15 min., IFB

Atomic Physics, Part 3: Nuclear Structure of the Atom, 16mm, b/w, 19 min., UEVA

Atomic Physics, Part 4: Discovery of the Neutron, 16mm, b/w, 22 min., UEVA

Exploring the Atomic Nucleus, 16mm, color, 12 min., Coronet

The Atom and Archaeology (Carbon-14 dating), 16mm, color, 25 min., HFC

Atomic Energy: Inside the Atom, 16mm, color, 13 min., EBEC

Fundamentals of Radioactivity, 16mm, b/w, 56 min., NAVC

Radioactivity Decay, 16mm, color, 3 min., OHSU

Radioactivity, 16mm, color, 13 min., MCGH

Laboratory:
Bernard and Epp: #42: The Laser

#47: The Characteristics of a Geiger Tube

#48: The Nature of Radioactive Emission

#49: Properties of Radioactive Radiation

#50: Measurement of Radioactive Half-Life

Preston: #26: Geiger-Mueller Counter: Radioactive Decay

#27: Half-Life

Computer Resources for Chapter 38

Programs:

1. *SCATTER: Nuclear Scattering*. Conduit. Apple II. Tutorial on nuclear scattering.
2. *Radioactivity: Half-life*. Phizphun. Apple II. Tutorial.

Computer Notes:

CHAPTER 38: LECTURE NOTES
NUCLEAR PHYSICS AND RADIOACTIVITY

Nuclear Structure (p. 824)

The Strong Nuclear Force and the Stability of the Nucleus (p. 826)

The Mass Defect of the Nucleus and Nuclear Binding Energy (p. 827)

Radioactivity (p. 830)

Conservation Laws

CHAPTER 38: LECTURE NOTES

Alpha Decay

Beta Decay

Gamma Decay

The Neutrino (p. 833)

Radioactive Decay and Activity (p. 834)

CHAPTER 38: LECTURE NOTES

Radioactive Dating (p. 836)

Radioactive Decay Series (p. 838)

Detectors of Radiation (p. 839)

CHAPTER 38: NEXT TIME NOTES

CHAPTER 39: TEACHING AIDS

IONIZING RADIATION, NUCLEAR ENERGY, AND ELEMENTARY PARTICLES

Transparencies:

Figure 39.6: Diagram of a nuclear power plant that uses a pressurized water reactor.

Figure 39.7: Fission and fusion considered in terms of the binding energy per nucleon.

Solved Problems:

Text Problem 3 is Study Guide Example 1.
Text Problem 23 is Study Guide Example 3.
Text Problem 31 is Study Guide Practice Problem 3.
Text Problem 13 is Study Guide Practice Problem 6.

Spreadsheets: None

Demonstrations:

Freier and Anderson MPa-1;
Hilton A-22, A-23;
Meiners 41-2.9

Films:

Fusion: The Ultimate Fire, 16mm, color, 14 min., BFA
Atomic Power Production, 16mm, color, 13 min., HFC
Energy: The Nuclear Alternative (Second Edition), 16mm, color, 22 min., CHUH
Fusion: The Electric and Infinite Future, 16mm, color, 22 min., DOC
Learning About Nuclear Energy (Second Edition), 16mm, color, 15 min., EBEC
Nuclear Power: Pro and Con, 16mm, color, 50 min., MCGH
Nuclear Radiation Fallout, 16mm, color, 15 min., CENCO
World of Enrico Fermi, 16mm, b/w, 46 min., HR
Everyday Radioactivity, 16mm, color, 21 min., STERLED
Short-Lived Radiosiotopes in Nuclear Medicine, 16mm, color, 27 min., NAVC
Basic Principles of Power Reactors, 16mm, color, 8.5 min., NAVC
Synchrotron, 16mm, color, 14 min., USAEC

Laboratory: None suggested

Computer Resources for Chapter 39

Computer Notes:

CHAPTER 39: LECTURE NOTES
IONIZING RADIATION, NUCLEAR ENERGY, AND ELEMENTARY PARTICLES

Biological Effects of Ionizing Radiation (p. 845)

Terms and Units

The Effects of Radiation on Humans

Induced Nuclear Reactions (p. 848)

Nuclear Fission (p. 850)

The Fission Process

CHAPTER 39: LECTURE NOTES

Chain Reaction

Nuclear Reactors (p. 852)

Basic Components

The Pressurized Water Reactor

The Breeder Reactor

Nuclear Fusion (p. 854)

CHAPTER 39: LECTURE NOTES

Elementary Particles (p. 857)

Setting the Stage

Neutrinos

Positrons and Antiparticles

Muons and Pions

Classification of Particles

Quarks

CHAPTER 39: NEXT TIME NOTES